Hydraulic factors in bridge design

Hydraulic factors in bridge design

R.V. FARRADAY, *G. Maunsell & Partners*

F.G. CHARLTON, *Hydraulics Research Station Limited*

Hydraulics Research
Wallingford

0614438X

Published by the Hydraulics Research Station Limited, Wallingford, Oxfordshire
Produced by Thomas Telford Ltd, 26–34 Old Street, London EC1P 1JH

British Library Cataloguing in Publication Data
Charlton, F. G.
    Hydraulic factors in bridge design.
    1. Bridges—Design   2. Hydraulic engineering
    I. Title   II. Farraday, R. V.
    624′.25   TG300

ISBN 0 946466 009

Set in English Times and Helios by MHL Typesetting Ltd, Coventry

Printed and bound in Great Britain by William Clowes (Beccles) Ltd, Beccles and London

624·25
FAR

Contents

x

Preface

The design of a bridge over a river demands that detailed attention should be paid not only to the route location, potential traffic flow and structural and foundation requirements, but also to the characteristics of the river flowing beneath. For this it is necessary to collect information on, and to understand the factors that govern, channel stability, water discharge and water levels, sediment discharge, scour and sediment deposition, and hydrodynamic forces. Predictions about what is likely to happen in particular circumstances then have to be made.

Information may be collected by aerial, hydrographic and hydraulic surveys; it may be understood by reference to recently determined and long-established principles of hydraulic civil engineering science; and predictions as to the future may be made following calculations or numerical or physical model studies.

This book covers all these aspects, some in considerable detail, with ample reference to the literature, and indicates how answers may be obtained to the questions that are likely to arise in practice. It is a book for the practising design engineer. It identifies the hydraulic aspects that characterise a river and provides guidance on assessing their influence on bridge design.

The book was written as part of a research programme undertaken by the Hydraulics Research Station Limited, Wallingford, in collaboration with G. Maunsell and Partners, Consulting Engineers, London. It draws spontaneously on the results of research built up over many years at Hydraulics Research Station Limited, correlated as necessary with that done elsewhere, and on the acknowledged design expertise of G. Maunsell and Partners.

The authors have taken care to arrange material in a form most suitable for the busy design engineer. Thus Chapter 9 draws together the results of the earlier chapters, examines the effects on bridge design, and suggests a step-by-step design procedure. Chapter 10 discusses case histories of some bridges selected to illustrate particular ideas. The final chapter suggests topics for further research.

The authors wish to acknowledge the advice and guidance they have received from their colleagues, notably A.J.M. Harrison, J.S. Burgess, J.A. Perkins and W.R. White (Hydraulics Research Station Limited), and J. Read and A. Sleigh (G. Maunsell and Partners).

Chapter 1

River morphology

Introduction

Rivers, which convey water in one direction only, as opposed to estuaries, which experience flow in two directions, fall into two categories—alluvial and incised. Alluvial rivers erode their banks, scour their beds and form their hydraulic geometry to suit the discharge, slope of valley and the sediment introduced from upstream. They have flood plains on either side of their channel and the flow sometimes overtops the channel banks to spread across the flood plain. Incised rivers behave in a similar way, but the topography exercises a greater constraint on the channel flow and geometry. Such rivers are narrower and deeper than the alluvial type, and rarely overtop their banks. Meander belt widths are also generally greater in relation to channel width than are those of alluvial rivers.

Sediment within channels of both river types is transported as both suspended load and bed load. The suspended load consists of fine material almost permanently in suspension, much of which will be material eroded from the catchment; this will have entered the river channel with the overland flow. The coarser fraction of the suspended load will be largely derived from the river bed and will be deposited when the flow decreases and the capacity of the river to carry sediment is reduced. The bed load, comprising mainly coarse material, is moved along the bed and is in almost continuous contact with it.

Channel stability

Rivers may be classified according to their stability: statically stable, dynamically stable, or unstable.

Statically stable rivers

These have reached a stage in their development when the forces of the flowing water are insufficient to scour the bed, erode the banks, or even transport significant quantities of sediment in suspension or as bed load. The boundaries of the river channel are inert for most of each year and the channel behaves as if it had rigid boundaries. Interference with the flow pattern, however, may cause local changes in the channel geometry.

Dynamically stable rivers

These are generally continually active, scouring and depositing material on the bed, eroding and depositing material on the banks, and transporting significant quantities of sediment. Although they change their channel shape over a short period, the changes are not progressive but vary about a mean condition. However, the pattern or plan form of such rivers does migrate, although it does not significantly change its shape unless there is a marked variation in the properties of the boundary material along the channel. The migrating channel pattern causes progressive erosion as the pattern moves downstream. Interference with the flow pattern of such rivers immediately causes local changes in channel geometry which may extend some distance upstream and downstream of the point of interference.

Unstable rivers

These usually transport large quantities of sediment, and are continually scouring and depositing material and eroding their banks. The deposited shoals deflect flow, causing the channels to change their shape, position and pattern progressively. The behaviour of such rivers is usually unpredictable and the rivers are difficult to control. Remedial works often include a major programme of catchment management, covering erosion control within the catchment, the construction of sediment traps in the upper reaches of the river, bank protection measures and flood embankment construction.

Channel pattern

The pattern or plan shape of a river is important, as it gives an indication of the degree and type of control which may be necessary to prevent the river from endangering bridge and approach works. There are three classes of pattern: straight, meandering, and braided.

Straight channels

Channels are rarely straight for more than about ten channel widths. If they are straight single channels, they are probably statically stable.

Meandering channels

These are very common, although a regular sinuous pattern is rare. Variations in the constitution of the bank material hinder or encourage the rate of bank erosion, causing unequal movement of the meander

2

along the river's length. The channels are usually dynamically stable. Their section fluctuates about a mean position as the pattern moves progressively downstream. The meander length of alluvial rivers is about 6 times the channel width, while the meander breadth can be up to 17 times the channel width. When the river is incised, the ratios are about 11 and 27 respectively.

Empirical relations for estimating meander length and breadth in sand or gravel bed rivers are available but the rate of meander migration varies widely and there is no reliable guide to estimate this rate. The following equations may be used to estimate meander length and breadth (references 1 and 6)

$$L_m = 65Q_D^{0.5} \tag{1}$$

$$B_m = 2.86L_m \text{ (rivers with flood plains)} \tag{2}$$

$$B_m = 2.2L_m \text{ (incised rivers)} \tag{3}$$

where L_m is the meander wave length, m; Q_D is the dominant discharge, m³/s, often taken as the equivalent of bankfull flow; B_m is the meander breadth, m.

Braided channels

These are usually unstable, being fed with larger quantities of sediment than they can transport. As a consequence, over short reaches they deposit sediment which steepens the gradient, allowing larger quantities of sediment to be carried. The deposited shoals often become so large that they deflect the flow, causing the channel to shift its position.

Effect of bridges on river regime

The introduction of structures into the river channel or flood plain affects both flow pattern and flow intensity, which in turn change the river morphology, the local channel geometry, and the relationship between water level and discharge.

Abutments and piers interfere with the flow pattern resulting in scour adjacent to the structure. Embankments within the flood plain interfere with natural drainage and divert flow from the flood plain into the river channel, causing an increase in the discharge intensity. The greater discharge intensity, enhanced by piers, increases scour depths and head loss through the bridge opening. The greater head loss raises upstream water levels and causes more frequent floods of greater intensity.

Hydraulic geometry of river channels

The hydraulic geometry of a river channel describes the channel width, depth, cross-sectional shape, gradient and alignment. It is dependent on

3

HYDRAULIC FACTORS IN BRIDGE DESIGN

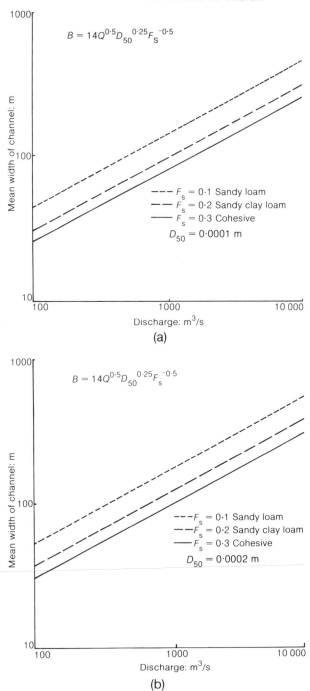

$$B = 14Q^{0.5}D_{50}^{0.25}F_S^{-0.5}$$

$F_S = 0.1$ Sandy loam
$F_S = 0.2$ Sandy clay loam
$F_S = 0.3$ Cohesive
$D_{50} = 0.0001$ m

(a)

$$B = 14Q^{0.5}D_{50}^{0.25}F_S^{-0.5}$$

$F_S = 0.1$ Sandy loam
$F_S = 0.2$ Sandy clay loam
$F_S = 0.3$ Cohesive
$D_{50} = 0.0002$ m

(b)

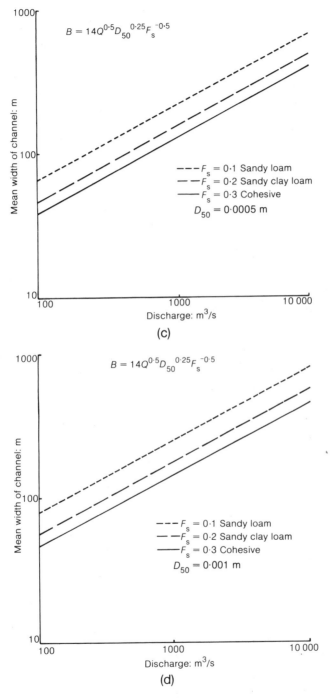

Fig. 1. Sand bed river—mean channel width

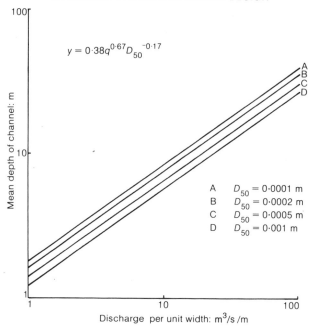

Fig. 2. Sand bed river—mean depth of channel

a number of factors which include discharge, characteristics of bed and bank material, the amount of sediment transported by the channel, and the ability of the channel to transport the quantities of sediment supplied from sources further upstream. There is no satisfactory method of calculating channel geometry which may be applied to all types of river. There are, however, many different empirical and semi-theoretical methods of analysis in use, each of which is restricted to channels of particular characteristics.

It is only possible within the scope of this book to summarise briefly the more important methods of computing the hydraulic geometry of statically stable and dynamically stable channels. It should be appreciated that the equations quoted below can only be a guide for computing hydraulic geometry, since variations in channel slope and sediment load may have a significant effect on the width and depth of flow as calculated using these equations.

Sand bed channels

The following equations have been deduced from the work of Blench[2]

$$B = 14Q^{0.5} D_{50}^{0.25} F_s^{-0.5} \tag{4}$$

$$y = 0.38q^{0.67} D_{50}^{-0.17} \tag{5}$$

6

$$q = Q/B$$

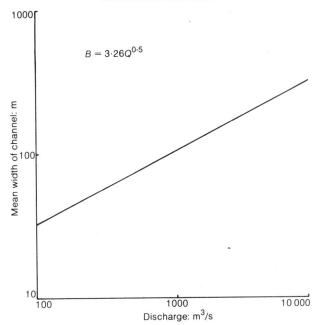

Fig. 3. Gravel bed river—mean width of channel

where B is the mean channel width, m; y is the mean depth of flow, m; Q is the equivalent steady discharge which would generate the same channel geometry, often assumed to be bankfull flow in alluvial channels. To estimate channel geometry under flood conditions the design flood flow may be used, m³/s; q is the discharge per unit width $= (Q/B)$, m³/s/m; D_{50} is the median size of bed material, m; F_s is the side factor to describe bank toughness (sandy loam, $F_s = 0.1$; silty clay loam, $F_s = 0.2$; cohesive banks, $F_s = 0.3$).

Figures 1(a)–(d) and 2 show the relation between channel width or depth and discharge as defined by Equations (4) and (5).

Gravel bed channels

The following equations have been deduced from research by Kellerhals[8]

$$B = 3 \cdot 26 Q^{0 \cdot 5} \tag{6}$$

$$y = 0 \cdot 47 q^{0 \cdot 8} D_{90}{}^{-0 \cdot 12} \tag{7}$$

where B, y, Q and q are defined as above and D_{90} is the size of bed material, m, such that 90% of the stones by number are smaller.

Figures 3 and 4 show the relations between width or depth and discharge as defined by Equations (6) and (7).

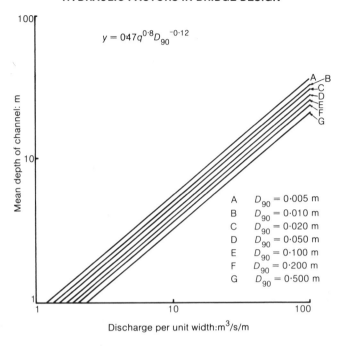

Fig. 4. Gravel bed river—mean depth of channel

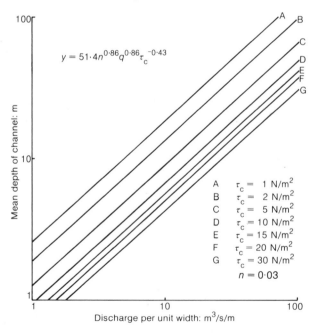

Fig. 5. Cohesive bed river—mean depth of channel

Table 1. Physical properties of clay

Voids ratio	2·0–1·2	1·2–0·6	0·6–0·3	0·3–0·2
Dry bulk density, kg/m³	880–1200	1200–1650	1650–2030	2030–2210
Saturated bulk density, kg/m³	1550–1740	1740–2030	2030–2270	2270–2370

Type of soil	Critical tractive stress, N/m²			
Sandy clay	1·9	7·5	15·7	30·2
Heavy clay	1·5	6·7	14·6	27·0
Clay	1·2	5·9	13·5	25·4
Lean clay	1·0	4·6	10·2	16·8

Cohesive bed channels

The resistance to scour of a cohesionless bed is due principally to the immersed weight of the particles. The resistance of cohesive materials, however, is more complex and depends on the surface physico-chemical characteristics, density and water quality. The only fairly reliable method of estimating scour is to measure the soil properties and to carry out model tests in a laboratory. Table 1, however, is given as a guide to assist in estimating the mean depth of flow in a cohesive bed channel, based on a description of the types and grading of the bed material and on the voids ratio, defined as the ratio of the volume of voids to the volume of solid material in a mass of soil. The bulk densities in Table 1 assume that the specific gravity of the particles is 2·64, and are related to the voids ratio by

$$\text{dry bulk density} = \frac{\rho s}{e + 1} \tag{8}$$

$$\text{saturated bulk density} = \frac{\rho (s + e)}{e + 1} \tag{9}$$

where ρ is the mass density of water, s is the specific gravity of the soil particles, and e is the voids ratio of the soil mass.

The depth of flow in a channel may be calculated assuming that scour will occur until a depth is reached such that the tractive stress on the bed equals the critical tractive stress. Thus

$$y = 51 \cdot 4 n^{0·86} q^{0·86} \tau_c^{-0·43} \tag{10}$$

where y is the mean depth of flow, m; n is the coefficient of roughness in Manning's equation; q is the discharge per unit width, m³/s/m; τ_c is the critical tractive stress for scour to occur, N/m².

Figure 5 shows a plot of Equation (10) assuming that $n = 0·03$.

9

Table 2. Multiplying factors for maximum channel depth

Location	Multiplying factor
Straight reach of channel	1·25
Moderate bend	1·50
Severe bend	1·75
Right-angled abrupt turn	2·0

Maximum channel depth

The foregoing equations allow the mean depth of flow, y, to be estimated. The maximum channel depth may be obtained by applying empirical multiplying factors to the mean depth. These factors are attributable to Lacey[9] and are given in Table 2. Neill[12] has suggested that the factor of 1·25 for straight reaches in alluvial streams should be increased to 1·5 where the dunes on the bed are moving.

References

1. Ackers, P. and Charlton, F.G. Meander geometry arising from varying flow. *J. Hydrol.*, 1970, **XI**, 287–314.
2. Blench, T. *Mobile bed fluviology*, University of Alberta Press, Edmonton, 1969.
3. Charlton, F.G. An appraisal of available data on gravel rivers. *Report No. INT 151*, Hydraulics Research Station, Wallingford, December 1975.
4. Charlton, F.G. *et al.* The hydraulic geometry of some gravel rivers in Britain. *Report No. IT 180*, Hydraulics Research Station, Wallingford, July 1978.
5. Henderson, F.M. Sediment transport. *Open channel flow*, ch. 10, Collier–Macmillan, London, 1966.
6. Inglis, C.C. Meanders and their bearing on river training. Institution of Civil Engineers, Maritime and Waterways Engineering Division meeting, 28 January 1947.
7. Jansen, P. Ph. *et al. Principles of river engineering*, Pitman, London, 1979.
8. Kellerhals, R. Stable channels with gravel paved beds. *Proc. Am. Soc. Civ. Engrs*, 1967, **93**, No. WW1, Feb., 63.
9. Lacey, G. Flow in alluvial channels with sandy mobile beds. *Proc. Instn Civ. Engrs*, 1958, **9**, Feb., 145–164; 1958, **11**, Oct., 219–251.
10. Lane, E.W. Design of stable channels. *Trans Am. Soc. Civ. Engrs*, 1955, **120**, 1234.
11. Leopold, L.B. *et al. Fluvial processes in geomorphology*, W.H. Freeman and Co., San Francisco, 1964.
12. Neill, C.R. *Guide to bridge hydraulics*, Roads and Transportation Association of Canada, University of Toronto Press, 1973.
13. Partheniades, E. River mechanics. *Erosion and deposition of cohesive materials*, ch. 25, 11 (ed. H.W. Shen), Fort Collins, Colorado, 1971.
14. Blench, T. *Civil engineering reference book* (eds E.H. Probst and J. Comrie), Butterworths, London, 1951.
15. Raudkivi, A.J. *Loose boundary hydraulics*, Pergamon Press, Oxford, 1967.

Further reading

Behaviour of sand bed channels, see references 2, 14, 9, 10, 15, 1
Behaviour of gravel bed channels, see references 8, 3, 4, 10, 5
Erosion and deposition of cohesive materials, see references 13, 10, 12
Channel patterns, see references 6, 7, 11

Chapter 2

Site reconnaissance survey

Introduction

Usually, the site for a road or rail bridge crossing will be restricted to certain reaches of the river through constraints imposed by the road or railway alignment. The choice of site must be made within these reaches and will avoid, wherever possible, locations which would necessitate costly river works.

Site selection

In statically stable rivers, in which the flow channel pattern and cross-section do not change significantly, the choice of a crossing site will be governed primarily by the main channel width and the proportion of flood plain flow to the total flow. First consideration should be given to those sites which have the narrowest main flow channels and the smallest proportion of flood plain flow.

Selection of suitable crossing sites is more difficult in dynamically stable rivers. Other than in rare situations where the flood plain is spanned completely by the bridge, some degree of training works will be required to stabilise the flow channel within the bridge waterway opening. Crossing sites where the channel may be controlled with a minimum of river training works should, therefore, be given first consideration. Often, sites may be found where outcrops of rock or inerodible bank material or artificial obstruction will reduce the requirement for training works, by restraining, or partly restraining, the lateral movement of the channel for some distance downstream. Less frequently, sites may be found where the channel is controlled by existing features so that oscillation is about a nodal point, usually at a crossover in the meander pattern, and training works will be minimal. In reaches where existing features provide little control over the channel position, training works will be necessary, and the choice will be for a crossing site at a bend or at a crossover. At bends the channel is narrower but deeper, particularly at the outside of the

12

bend; at crossovers, the channel is wider and shallower. The most suitable location can be determined only after giving overall consideration to the channel geometry, the requirement for training works and the type of bridge construction.

Bridge crossings over unstable channels nearly always necessitate extensive river works to restrict the river within the bridge waterway opening. If the unstable channel is in the form of an alluvial fan which aggrades and shifts, a longer rail or road route to a crossing point upstream of the apex of the fan might prove to be economically more viable than a crossing within the fan, which would inevitably necessitate construction of substantial training works.

It is with these broad concepts in mind that the site reconnaissance survey should be planned and undertaken.

Reconnaissance survey

The objective of the reconnaissance survey is to gain a general appreciation of the behaviour of the river by examining available records and by field inspection. Information on the following topics should be collected.

(a) River channel regime. It should be determined whether the river has a wide flood plain, or whether it is incised with little or no flood plain.

(b) River channel stability. It should be determined whether the river is statically stable, dynamically stable or unstable.

(c) River channel flow pattern. If it is sinuous, determine whether the channel migration is active.

(d) Range of water levels, particularly high-water levels and their frequency of occurrence.

(e) Range of discharges, particularly flood discharges and their frequency of occurrence.

(f) Width of waterway, width of flood plain, meander length and meander width.

(g) Type and grading of bed material.

(h) Type of material composing the river banks.

(i) Location of any natural outcrops of inerodible rock which may restrict channel movement.

Examination of available records

Information on the above topics is usually available from a variety of sources, including the following.

Topographic survey maps

These provide information on the channel pattern, channel width and flood plain. If older survey maps are also available, comparisons may reveal valuable information about channel stability, meander migration and the presence of rock outcrops which restrict channel movement. Apart from the usual sources, the older maps may be found in public libraries, universities, private libraries, geographical societies, etc.

Geological survey maps and land use survey maps

These may be available in government departments concerned with geology, agriculture, forestry, soil erosion, soil and water management and conservation, irrigation and hydro-electric power.

Aerial surveys or aerial photographs including oblique photographs

When photographs taken at intervals are available these are an even more valuable source providing, in addition to channel geometry, information on channel stability and possibly flooding. Aerial photographs often show earlier positions of the river channel, and to obtain the maximum benefit, advice from a specialist on the interpretation of aerial photographs should be sought.

Satellite photographs

The linear scale of these photographs is usually too small for an accurate assessment of channel width. They may, however, be used to establish channel pattern, width of flood plain and, since photographs have been taken at intervals over a number of years, channel stability and extent of flooding.

Plans and records of the construction and maintenance of river training and flood control works

If there are engineering works along the channel, the problems associated with the construction and maintenance of those works may give an insight into the behaviour of the channel.

Field inspection

The purpose of the field inspection is to gain a better understanding of river behaviour by inspecting the channel boundaries, preferably at low stages of river flow. The information gathered will enable river behaviour due to changes in existing conditions to be predicted, hydraulic characteristics which will have an effect on the choice of general bridge design to be identified, and the extent of river training and bank protection schemes to be determined.

The field inspection should establish

(a) type and grading of bed material
(b) existence of shoals and their composition

(*c*) the material forming the bank
(*d*) vegetation on the bank
(*e*) steepness of banks and evidence of bank erosion
(*f*) erosion pockets and embayments in the bank
(*g*) existence of inerodible rock
(*h*) debris marks on shrubs, trees or banks which may indicate the water level of recent floods
(*i*) watermarks on walls, jetties and piers which indicate recent high-water levels.

When the assessment of the survey information has been completed, acceptable sites for a bridge crossing from the fluvial aspect may be chosen. Detailed field surveys of the site will then be necessary.

Chapter 3

Hydrographic and hydraulic surveys

Introduction

Following the selection of suitable sites for the bridge crossing, hydrographic and hydraulic surveys must be planned to obtain the data necessary to calculate the width of the bridge opening, depth of scour, hydrodynamic forces on piers, and backwater. The following sections summarise the general survey requirements and may be used as a basis for a programme for site investigation.

Hydrographic survey

The hydrographic survey should ideally include the following. Cross-sections of the river channel and the flood plain should be surveyed along the line of the proposed bridge crossing and at distances of $0 \cdot 5$, 1, 2, 4, 6 and 12 channel widths upstream and at distances of $0 \cdot 5$, 1, 2 and 4 channel widths downstream of the crossing. All levels should be reduced to a common datum. If backwater is unlikely to be a problem (e.g. the channel may be steep, the bridge opening very wide, or flooding would cause no inconvenience) then the extent of the cross-sectional survey may be reduced.

The plan form of the channel and flood plain should be obtained from existing reliable survey maps. If these are not available a traverse should be run along both banks of the channel to establish the channel pattern. The traverse should extend for a distance of not less than 12 channel widths upstream and 6 channel widths downstream of the crossing.

The grading of the bed material should be determined at not less than four stations across the river, at the site of the crossing, and at two stations (the third points), on the cross-sections at $0 \cdot 5$ and $1 \cdot 0$ channel width upstream.

Samples of the sediment should be taken from the river bed and at intervals below it, down to a depth of $1 \cdot 5$ times the depth of the channel. It is recommended that a rough estimate of scour depth be made to assist in choosing the depth to which samples should be taken. The method of sampling and grading is discussed below.

Hydraulic survey

The topographic features of a river, other than bed level, do not usually change very rapidly. It is therefore possible, in a single survey, to gather enough reliable data on river bank and flood plain levels. The hydraulic characteristics of a river are, however, continually changing and it is only by frequent surveys extending over a long period that sufficient data may be gathered for a statistical analysis to provide a guide to the extreme values which will affect the design and safety of the bridge. It is rare for a bridge to be sited at or near a long-established discharge gauging station and, hence, as soon as a bridge is proposed, a gauging station should be established near the site of the proposed crossing.

The discharge passing through the site of the bridge opening should be measured at a number of different stages of flow. Each discharge measurement should be related to a date, time and water level, the latter being reduced to the standard datum used for the cross-sectional surveys.

Velocities in both magnitude and direction should be measured at about ten or more points across the river channel on several occasions at the higher stages of flow. These velocity measurements may be part of the discharge measurement programme referred to above.

Float tracks should be observed on at least two occasions at high stages of flow. At least six float tracks spaced across the channel should be observed, covering a distance from three channel widths upstream to one channel width downstream of the proposed site.

Water surface slope should be measured over a range of discharges. Water-level measuring stations should be spaced sufficiently far apart to give the required accuracy in slope, taking into account the accuracy of measurement of water level. If the overall uncertainty in the measurement of water level at the two stations is about $0 \cdot 05$ m, including any error in levelling between the stations, and the required accuracy in slope is 5%, then the minimum distance between stations should be as shown in Table 3.

Table 3. Minimum distance between water level measuring stations

Water surface slope	Minimum distance between stations, m
$0 \cdot 002$	500
$0 \cdot 001$	1000
$0 \cdot 0002$	5000

Table 4. Particle size classification

	Grain size, mm						
0·002	0·006	0·02	0·06	0·2	0·6	2·0	
	Fine Medium Coarse			Fine Medium Coarse			
Clay	Silt			Sand			Gravel

Sampling and grading procedure

The procedures discussed below vary according to the type of bed material. Names have been assigned to bed materials according to the classification in Table 4.

Silt and clay

Undisturbed samples of the material on the bed and at various levels below the bed should be extracted using a sampling tube. Parts of each sample should be used to obtain the bulk density and moisture content, the liquid limit and the plastic limit, and the distribution of particle sizes.

Sand

Material on the bed may be extracted using a spade, whilst material at depth should be extracted using an auger or a sampling tube with a basket shoe or flap valve. The samples should each be dried, sieved and weighed to establish the grading by weight.

Gravel

The stones on the surface should be sampled by setting out a grid of 1 m squares about 9 m long by 9 m wide. A total of about 100 stones lying below the intersecting lines of the grid are then removed. Each stone has three mutually orthogonal axes, the major, the intermediate and the minor. The length of the intermediate axis of each stone is measured, and the stones are graded by number, not weight, according to the length of the intermediate axis.

The gravel occurring at a shallow depth below the bed may be extracted as a bulk sample by digging a pit. These samples can most easily be graded after drying by sieving and weighing if the particles are small, and graded by number if the particles are large.[6] Material at depths too great to be excavated by digging a pit should be extracted using an auger not less than 100 mm in diameter. Grading is carried out as for bulk samples above.

References
1. Ackers, P. *et al. Weirs and flumes for flow measurement*, John Wiley, Chichester, 1978.
2. Adams, J. Gravel size analysis from photographs. *Proc. Am. Soc. Civ. Engrs*, 1979, **105**, No. HY10, Oct., 1247.
3. BRITISH STANDARDS INSTITUTION. Methods of measurement of liquid flow in open channels. *BS 3680*, BSI, London.
   Part 1. Glossary of terms, 1979.
   Part 2A. Dilution methods: constant rate injection.
   Part 2B. Dilution methods: sudden injection method.
   Part 2C. Dilution methods: radioisotope techniques.
   Part 3A. Velocity area methods, 1981.
   Part 3B. Establishment and operation of a gauging station, 1981.
   Part 3C. Stage discharge relation, 1981.
   Part 3D. Moving boat method, 1982.
   Part 3E. Ultrasonic method.
   Part 3F. Data for the determination of errors.
   Part 4A. Thin plate weirs, 1980.
   Part 4B. Triangular profile weirs, 1980.
   Part 4C. Flumes, 1980.
   Part 4D. Compound gauging structures, 1980.
   Part 4E. Rectangular broad crested weirs, 1980.
   Part 4F. Round nosed horizontal crest weirs, 1980.
   Part 4G. Flat V weirs, 1980.
   Part 5. Slope area method, 1980.
   Part 7. Water level measuring devices, 1980.
   Part 8A. Current meters incorporating a rotating element.
   Part 8B. Current meter suspension equipment.
   Part 8D. Cableway system, 1980.
   Part 8E. Ultrasonic velocity meters.
   Part 8F. Echo sounders, 1981.
   Part 9A. Water level instruments: specification for the installation and performance of pressure-actuated liquid level measuring equipment.
   Part 10A. Sediment load samples, 1980.
   Part 10B. Methods of measuring sediment load, 1980.
   Part 10C. Bed material sampling, 1980.
   Part 10D. Methods for analysis of sediment, calculation of uncertainty of flow rate.
4. Charlton, F.G. Measuring flow in open channels, a review of methods. *Report No. 75*, Construction Industry Research and Information Association, London, 1978.
5. Herschy, R.W. (ed.). *Hydrometry*, John Wiley, Chichester, 1978.
6. Kellerhals, R. and Bray, D.I. Sampling procedures for coarse fluvial sediments. *Proc. Am. Soc. Civ. Engrs*, 1971, **97**, No. HY8, Aug., 1165.
7. Lambe, T.W. *Soil testing for engineers*, John Wiley, New York and London, 1951.

Further reading
Glossary of terms, see reference 3 (Part 1)

Sediment sampling and grading
    Fine sediment, see reference 3 (Parts 10C, 10D)
    Gravel, see references 6, 2
Measurement of water level, see references 3 (Parts 3B, 7), 4, 3 (Part 9A)
Measurement of velocity, see references 4, 5, 3 (Parts 8A, 8B, 8D, 8E)
Measurement of discharge
    Velocity area, see references 3 (Parts 3A, 3B), 4, 5, 3 (Parts 3D, 8F)
    Slope area, see references 3 (Parts 5, 3B), 4
    Dilution gauging, see references 3 (Parts 2A, 2B, 2C, 3B), 4, 5
    Stage discharge, see references 3 (Parts 3C, 3B), 4
    Slope stage discharge, see references 3 (Part 3B), 4
    Weirs, see references 1, 5, 3 (Part 3B), 4, 3 (Parts 4A, 4B, 4C, 4D, 4E, 4F, 4G)
    Flumes, see references 1, 5, 3 (Part 3B), 4
    Electromagnetic, see references 3 (Part 3B), 4
    Existing facilities, see references 5, 4, 3 (Part 3B)

Chapter 4

Estimation of design discharge and water level

Introduction

This chapter describes methods of assessing flood discharge and water level at the bridge site and the effect which the bridge has on water level. The design discharge should be selected having regard for the probability of the occurrence of greater values of discharge and the reliability of the data from which it was determined.

Flood return period

In assessing the return period of the design flood, such factors as possible loss of life and economic dislocation due to failure have to be set against the additional capital cost of a bridge designed for a longer return period. However, it is the nature of the problem that there can be no guarantee that in a case of a bridge designed for an estimated 1000-year flood, for example, the design discharge would not be exceeded in the first year of the structure's lifetime, although the probability of such an event is extremely small. For situations in the UK, George[9] has suggested the guidelines presented in Table 5.

Methods of assessing design discharge and water level

There are five main methods of estimating the design discharge and corresponding water level, depending on the field data available, as

Table 5. Design flood return periods

Bridge situation	Suggested return period
Bridge crossing valley immediately downstream of a community	1000 years
Motorway and trunk road bridges	150 years
Rural road bridges	30 years
Submersible bridges	5 years

Table 6. Estimation of flood discharge

Method	1	2	3	4	5
Data from field	Regular discharge and water level measurements at bridge site	Regular discharge and water level measurements at a gauging site Simultaneous water level measurements at gauging site and bridge site	Rainfall intensity–duration measurements in catchment Rainfall records at several stations in catchment for the same storms Topographic maps Geological maps showing soil type Maps showing type of vegetation River cross-sections and gradient	Rainfall intensity–duration measurements in catchment Rainfall records at several stations in catchment for the same storms Discharge hydrographs associated with rainfall hydrographs River cross-sections and gradient	Flood discharge formulae for catchment (simple formulae, synthetic unit hydrograph formulae, etc.) River cross-sections and gradient
Analyses	(a) Stage discharge relationship at bridge (b) Extrapolation of stage discharge relationship (c) Frequency analysis of discharge data (d) Selection of design discharge and water level	(a) Stage discharge relationship at bridge (b) Extrapolation of stage discharge relationship (c) Frequency analysis of discharge data (d) Selection of design discharge and water level	(a) Frequency analysis of rainfall data (b) Rainfall intensity–duration relation (c) Rainfall intensity–area relation (d) Rainfall intensity–runoff computation (e) Computation of water level	(a) Frequency analysis of rainfall data (b) Rainfall intensity–duration relation (c) Rainfall intensity–area relation (d) Rainfall intensity–runoff relation (e) Synthesis of unit hydrograph (f) Computation of water level	(a) Flood formulae (b) Computation of water level

summarised in Table 6. It is beyond the scope of this book to discuss them in detail and the following subsections are intended only as a guide. For a more detailed treatment, the reader is referred to the references.

Method 1

This method is applicable when there are regular discharge and water level measurements at the site of the proposed bridge over a period of several years, preferably not less than about ten years.

Stage discharge relationship

The discharge and water level measurements which have been reduced to a common datum (the stage) are tabulated. The datum is that used for both hydrographic and topographic surveys. The table should also include the date of observations and whether the water level was steady, rising or falling. The discharge and water level are plotted on logarithmic graph paper. Provided that there is no evidence of a systematic change in the stage discharge relation with time (i.e. shifting control) a smooth curve may be drawn through the plotted points.

Extrapolation of stage discharge relationship

The extrapolation of a stage discharge relationship beyond the measured values is difficult and subject to appreciable error, because channel sections may change significantly as the discharge increases. The change in section may be due in part to flow over a flood plain and in part to scour of the bed. The former can be estimated fairly easily, but the latter is very difficult to estimate.

A stage discharge curve may be extrapolated by extending the plotted curve, provided that there is no discontinuity in the relationship of depth to area of cross-section and no scour occurs. Such a discontinuity is likely when the bankfull discharge is expected.

A stage discharge curve may also be extrapolated by using a suitable channel flow equation (e.g. Manning's equation)

$$Q = (A/n)R^{0.67}S^{0.50} \qquad (11)$$

Assuming that no scour occurs and that $S^{0.5}/n$ is constant and substituting A/P for R in Equation (11)

$$Q = JA^{1.67}P^{-0.67} \qquad (12)$$

If the channel is wide, $R = y$ and from Equation (11)

$$Q = JAy^{0.67} \qquad (13)$$

where Q is the discharge, m³/s; A is the area of cross-section, m²; R is the hydraulic radius, m, $= (A/P)$; S is the hydraulic gradient; P is the wetted

23

perimeter, m; y is the mean depth of flow, m; n is the hydraulic roughness; $J = S^{0.5}/n$.

If it is expected that appreciable bed scour will occur, then for any chosen water level, (a) the flow over the flood plain is calculated using a suitable channel flow equation assuming no scour, (b) the flow within the channel is estimated using an appropriate mobile bed flow equation, assuming various depths of scour, and comparing the results with the stage discharge relation obtained for smaller discharges. The method is approximate only.

Frequency analysis of discharge data

Estimation of the magnitude of a flood discharge for a long return period generally necessitates extrapolating beyond the range of measured data. The procedure adopted will depend upon the assumptions made regarding the theoretical frequency distribution of the events. Basically, the maximum flood measured each year over the period of records is listed in order of magnitude. The duration of each flood depends on the size of the river and the rate of rise and fall of floods. In large rivers where the change in discharge over a day may be small, the daily flow may be used; in smaller rivers an hourly flow or flow over an even shorter period may be chosen.

The recurrence interval of each annual flood discharge is calculated by

$$T_r = \frac{r + 1}{m} \tag{14}$$

where T_r is the return period in years, r is the number of years' records, m is the order of ranking ($m = 1$ for maximum measured flood, $m = r$ for minimum measured flood).

The discharge is then plotted against the occurrence interval on simple graph paper, linear logarithmic paper, normal probability paper, logarithmic normal probability paper or Gumbel–Powell probability paper. Since it is sometimes difficult to extrapolate points which lie on a curve, the plot in which the points appear to lie most nearly on a straight line should be chosen and the line of best fit drawn through the points. The extrapolation of this line will permit the estimation of the discharge corresponding to a chosen return period.

It has been suggested above that where extreme floods are to be estimated, annual flood peaks should be used. Sometimes analyses are made using all floods above a chosen magnitude. This produces a partial duration series with return periods shorter than those derived from annual series. For data between one and ten years' duration, for example, the return periods may be between $0 \cdot 43$ and $0 \cdot 95$ of the return period derived from an annual series.[13]

Selection of design discharge and water level

The design discharge is obtained from the extrapolated discharge frequency curve for the return period selected. The corresponding water level is then read off from the extrapolated stage discharge curve.

Method 2

This method is applicable when there are regular discharge and water level measurements at a station on the river other than at the site of the proposed bridge, over a period of years, preferably not less than ten years. In addition, simultaneous water level measurements at the discharge station and the bridge site over a period covering as wide a range of water levels as possible are required.

Stage discharge relationship

The discharge and the water level measurements are tabulated as in Method 1. The simultaneous water level measurements, reduced to the same datum, are also tabulated. The simultaneous water level data are plotted on graph paper, differentiating between those measured during rising, falling, and steady periods of flow. A graphical relation is established and the water levels measured at the gauging station converted to equivalent levels at the proposed bridge site. The stage discharge curve for the bridge site is plotted as described under Method 1 using the discharge measurements and the deduced values of water level.

Extrapolation of stage discharge relationship

The synthetic stage discharge curve developed for the bridge site is extrapolated as described under Method 1.

Frequency analysis of discharge data

The annual flood maxima are listed and plotted as described in Method 1 using the discharge records from the regular gauging site.

Selection of design discharge and water level

The design discharge is chosen as in Method 1, and using the extrapolated theoretical stage discharge relation for the bridge site, the corresponding water level is obtained.

Method 3

This method is based on the method proposed by Richards[18] and is intended for use in catchments which have a main channel and only minor tributaries. The data available include

(*a*) rainfall intensity–duration measurements for several years (preferably not less than ten years) at one station which is representative of the rainfall conditions in the catchment; a more reliable prediction of discharge will result if data from several such stations are available

(b) rainfall records at several stations in the catchment for the same storms or, alternatively, a graph of the ratio of average rainfall intensity over an area to the intensity at a point against the area covered by the average rainfall intensity

(c) topographic maps showing the size, shape and contours of the catchment and the type of vegetation

(d) plan showing type of soil in the catchment.

Frequency analysis of rainfall data

The annual maximum one-hour duration rainfalls should be listed in descending order of magnitude. The return period of each event is then calculated from Equation (14). The hourly rainfall is next plotted against the return period using log-log paper and log-probability paper. A curve is drawn through the plotted points. The simpler of the two curves to extrapolate is then used to estimate the hourly rainfall for the required return period.

Rainfall intensity–duration relation

The following relation is assumed to be valid for the extreme rainfall conditions which occur within the catchment

$$I = \frac{H}{T + 1} \tag{15}$$

where I is the rainfall intensity at a point within the catchment, mm/h; T is the duration of storm, h; H is the rainfall constant, mm.

Substituting in the above equation for the point rainfall intensity of the required return period, the rainfall constant H is obtained.

Rainfall intensity–area relation

The average rainfall intensity over an area is less than the intensity at a point within that area. If a relation has been previously established between these values, then the average intensity over the catchment may be calculated from

$$i = If(a) \tag{16}$$

where i is the average rainfall intensity over a given area, mm/h; I is the rainfall intensity at a point within that area, mm/h; $f(a)$ is the rainfall reduction factor for the given area.

If this information is not available, the location of all rainfall stations within the catchment should be plotted on a map. The Thiessen polygon[13,14]

Table 7. Runoff coefficients

	Runoff coefficient K	
Type of catchment	Large catchment	Small catchment
Rocky and impermeable	0·8	1·0
Slightly permeable, bare	0·6	0·8
Slightly permeable, partly cultivated or covered with vegetation	0·4	0·6
Cultivated absorbent soil	0·3	0·4
Sandy absorbent soil	0·2	0·3
Heavy soil	0·1	0·2

is drawn for each station. For each of several storms the rainfall intensity is calculated for the whole catchment, whence

$$f(a) = \frac{i}{I} \tag{17}$$

Rainfall intensity–runoff computation

From a topographic survey map of the catchment area of the river upstream of the proposed bridge site, the following information is extracted

(a) the slope of the main stream over a length between 10% and 85% of the length of stream upstream of the bridge, making allowance for waterfalls and unusually steep slopes
(b) maximum length of the catchment from the bridge site
(c) area and shape of the catchment
(d) characteristics of the catchment with regard to permeability and vegetation.

From the description of the catchment and using Table 7 the runoff coefficient K is estimated.[18] Knowing the values of K and H, the coefficient C is calculated from

$$C = 0·706(KH - 10·16)^{-0·42} \tag{18}$$

The time of concentration is then calculated from

$$\frac{t^3}{t+1} = \frac{C L_c^2 N}{K S H f(a)} \tag{19}$$

where t is the time of concentration, h; L_c is the length of catchment, km; C is the coefficient; K is the runoff coefficient; S is the average slope of main stream omitting waterfalls and unusually steep slopes; H is the rainfall coefficient, mm; N is the factor based on shape of storm (assume $N = 1 \cdot 1$); $f(a)$ is the area reduction factor for rainfall intensity.

The average rainfall intensity is calculated from

$$i = \frac{H}{t + 1} f(a) \qquad (20)$$

and the discharge from

$$Q = 0 \cdot 278 \, K \, i \, a \qquad (21)$$

where Q is the discharge, m³/s; i is the average rainfall intensity over catchment for storm of t hours' duration, mm/h; a is the catchment area, km².

Computation of water level

The foregoing computations result in a discharge of the required return period. In order to calculate the corresponding water level, a flow formula appropriate to the bed material of the channel is chosen (see Chapter 1) and the depth of flow corresponding to the discharge, width, slope and type of bed material is calculated.

If flow is above bankfull, the flow at bankfull must be calculated and then, using a flow equation suitable for flow over a flood plain (e.g. Manning and Darcy), the depth of flow over the flood plain is calculated. Knowing the elevation of the top of the bank and the depth of flow over the bank, the elevation of the water surface corresponding to the design discharge is deduced.

Method 4

This method is applicable when the following data are available.

(*a*) Duration measurements for several years (preferably not less than about ten) at one station which is representative of the rainfall conditions over the catchment. A more reliable prediction of runoff will result if data from several such stations are available.

(*b*) Several sets of measurements over a range of discharges to provide a record of rainfall hydrographs and the corresponding discharge hydrograph at the proposed bridge site.

Frequency analysis of rainfall data

The procedure outlined in Method 3 is followed.

Rainfall intensity–duration relation

The procedure outlined in Method 3 is followed.

Rainfall intensity–area relation

The procedure outlined in Method 3 is followed.

Rainfall intensity–runoff relation

Unless there exist records of peak discharge measurements or estimations over approximately a ten-year period, it is not possible to determine the return period of discharge. Rainfall data are, however, often available. If the return period for rainfall intensities can be established, together with a relation between the volume of rainfall and the volume of runoff, then it is possible to calculate the return period for the runoff discharge.

From the rainfall hydrographs for the same storm recorded at several stations in the catchment, the total volume of rainfall is calculated using the Thiessen polygons referred to for the area relation in Method 3.

To obtain the discharge hydrograph for the same storm, the base flow is established and the runoff volume and duration then calculated. The procedure is repeated for several storms to obtain a relation between rainfall volume and runoff volume. From this, a runoff volume for the required return period is established.

Unit hydrograph analysis

From the records of discharge hydrographs for storms of reasonably uniform intensity and required duration, the base flow is separated from the total flow and unit hydrographs deduced from the resulting direct runoff. An average unit hydrograph is then prepared from unit hydrographs of the same duration to improve the accuracy. This unit hydrograph is then used to compute the peak flow resulting from the volume of rainfall corresponding to the selected return period.

The duration of unit hydrographs is complex and cannot be adequately summarised in this book. References 13, 22 and 23 at the end of this chapter contain details of the methods of calculation. Other information on unit hydrographs is listed in the references.

Computations of water level

The design discharge is derived from the unit hydrograph and the corresponding water level as described in Method 3.

Method 5

This method is applicable when the following are available

(*a*) a flood formula applicable to the area in which the proposed bridge is to be sited
(*b*) cross-sectional and longitudinal surveys of the river channel.

Flood formulae

It is essential that the flood formula chosen for the estimation of discharge is appropriate to the catchment of the river to be crossed. The formula should also provide an estimate of discharge for the required return period, and specify whether the discharge is an instantaneous peak or an average flow over a given period.

Formulae vary in complexity from the simple relation between discharge and catchment area (reference 8, Chapter III, reference 13, Chapter 20), to the complex relations which attempt to include several catchment and hydrological characteristics that affect the magnitude of the flood flow.[5] In some cases solutions may be presented in graphical form.[8] For situations in the UK, references 11, 15 and 20 will be particularly useful.

Computations of water level

The water level corresponding to the chosen value of design discharge is determined as described in Method 4.

Effect of bridge structure on water level

It is rarely economically feasible to bridge the river in one span. More usually, piers will be located within the main flow channel and embankments will encroach into the flood plain. These will obstruct the flow and cause upstream water levels to rise above the free discharge level.

The amount by which the level rises above the free discharge level, or backwater, may be calculated by the method given in references 1 and 10. The graphs and tables presented therein are too numerous and detailed to be condensed usefully within this book, and the following is therefore limited to a description of what can be taken into consideration by the calculation method

(*a*) incised or flood plain rivers
(*b*) eccentric location of flow channel within the flood plain
(*c*) skewed orientation of bridge crossing
(*d*) a variety of pier geometries
(*e*) the effect of scour on backwater
(*f*) discharge through partially submerged bridges
(*g*) discharge for flow across submerged roadway embankments.

References

1. Bradley, J.N. Hydraulics of bridge waterways. *Hydraulic Design Series No. 1*, Bureau of Public Roads, 2 edn, 1972.
2. British Standards Institution. Methods of measurement of liquid flow in open channels. *BS 3680 Part 3C, stage discharge relation*, BSI, London, 1981.
3. Chow, Ven Te. Statistical and probability analysis of hydrologic data. *Handbook of applied hydrology*, Section 8–I, (Ven Te Chow (ed.)),

McGraw-Hill, New York and London, 1964.
4. Chow, Ven Te. Statistical and probability analysis of hydrologic data. *Handbook of applied hydrology*, Section 8–IV, (Ven Te Chow (ed.)), McGraw-Hill, New York and London, 1964.
5. Chow, Ven Te. Runoff. *Handbook of applied hydrology*, Section 14, (Ven Te Chow (ed.)), McGraw-Hill, New York and London, 1964.
6. Colombi, J.S. The modified Richards method of flood estimation. *Proc. Instn Civ. Engrs*, Part 2, 1978, **65**, June, 299–306; Part 2, 1980, **69**, June, 565–570.
7. Dawdy, D.R. and Matalas, N.C. Statistical and probability analysis of hydrologic data. *Handbook of applied hydrology*, Section 8–III, (Ven Te Chow (ed.)), McGraw-Hill, New York and London, 1964.
8. Economic Commission on Asia and the Far East. Envelope frequency relations for maximum floods in monsoon areas of the ECAFE region. *Water Resources J.*, 1970, June.
9. George, A.B. Devon floods and the waterways of bridges. *Proc. Instn Civ. Engrs*, Part 2, 1982, **73**, Mar., 125–134.
10. Henderson, F.M. *Open channel flow*, Collier–Macmillan, London, 1966.
11. Institution of Civil Engineers. *Flood studies report—five years on*, Thomas Telford, London, 1981.
12. Lewis, G. A statistical estimation of flood flows. *Proc. Instn Civ. Engrs*, Part 2, 1979, **67**, Sept., 841–844.
13. Linsley, R.K. *et al. Applied hydrology*, McGraw-Hill, New York and London, 1949.
14. Linsley, R.K. *et al. Hydrology for engineers*, McGraw-Hill, New York and London, 1958.
15. Natural Environment Research Council. *Flood studies report*, NERC, London, 1975.
16. Poots, A.D. and Cochrane, S.R. Design flood estimation for bridges, culverts and channel improvement works on small rural catchments. *Proc. Instn Civ. Engrs*, Part 1, 1979, **66**, Nov., 663–666; Part 1, 1980, **68**, May, 317–322.
17. Reich, B.M. Short duration rainfall intensity estimates and other design aids for regions of sparse data. *J. Hydrol.*, 1963, **I**, Mar., 3–28.
18. Richards, B.D. *Flood estimation and control*, Chapman and Hall, London, 1955.
19. Snyder, W.M. Hydrograph analysis by the method of least squares. *Proc. Am. Soc. Civ. Engrs*, 1955, **81**, Paper 793.
20. Sutcliffe, J.V. Methods of flood estimation. A guide to the flood studies report. *Report No. 49*, Institution of Hydrology, Wallingford, 1978.
21. Whisler, B.A. and Smith, C.J. Estimation of frequency of rare floods. *Proc. Am. Soc. Civ. Engrs*, **83**, Paper 1200.
22. Williams, G.R. Engineering hydraulics. *Hydrology*, ch. IV (H. Rouse (ed.)), John Wiley, New York; Chapman and Hall, London, 1950.
23. Wilson, E.M. *Engineering hydrology*, Macmillan, 2 edn, London, 1974.
24. Yeudjevich, V.M. Statistical and probability analysis of hydrologic data. *Handbook of applied hydrology*, Section 8–II (Ven Te Chow (ed.)), McGraw-Hill, New York and London, 1964.

Further reading

Stage discharge relationship, see references 2, 10, 14, 13
Shifting control, see references 14, 13
Extrapolation of stage discharge relation, see references 14, 13
Frequency analysis of rainfall records, see references 14, 13, 23, 3, 24, 7, 4, 22, 17
Thiessen polygon, see references 14, 13
Frequency analysis of discharge records, see references 14, 13, 23, 3, 24, 7, 4, 12, 21
Unit hydrographs, see references 23, 14, 13, 22, 5, 10, 19
Estimation of runoff from rainfall, see references 18, 6, 22
Flood formulae, see references 5, 20, 15, 11, 8, 16, 18
Backwater, see references 10, 1
Flood return periods, see reference 9

Chapter 5

Local scour at bridge crossings

Introduction

In the design of piers, abutments, training works and temporary works for bridges over rivers, the assessment of the amount by which the bed is lowered adjacent to the structure as a result of scour needs careful consideration. Scour at bridge crossings may be divided into two main categories, general and local.

In the context of this book the general scour depth refers to the depth to which the bed is scoured in the bridge waterway, below the natural upstream bed level. If the waterway width is sufficiently wide not to restrict normal flow in the river, the river is said to be unconfined, and natural river depths prevail. Depths in the unconfined waterways of meandering rivers will therefore vary greatly as the main flow channel migrates across the width of the waterway. If the waterway width is restricted to prevent channel migration, the river is said to be confined and the flow channel is stabilised. In this book, local scour means the lowering of the river bed adjacent to structures, below the general scour level.

A further category of scour is the lowering of a river bed resulting from man-made changes to the river regime upstream or downstream of the bridge crossing, other than those directly associated with the bridge crossing, e.g. gravel mining, damming, reservoir regulation. Detailed treatment of this can be found in references 11 and 12.

Methods for assessing general scour depths have been described in Chapter 1 and the present chapter will concentrate on the methods of assessing local scour at piers, abutments and training works. The same methods can be applied to temporary works situations.

Local scour at bridge piers
Mechanism of scour

Local scour around piers is the result of vortex systems which develop as the river flow is deflected around the pier. The main vortex system

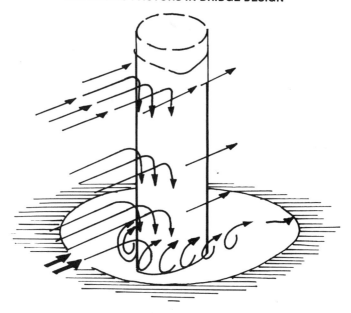

Fig. 6. Horseshoe vortex formation at a cylindrical pier

which contributes to the formation of scour holes originates at the upstream nose of the pier where the flow acquires a downward or diving component in elevation, which reverses direction in plan at the stream bed. As bed material is removed by the flow, a spiral roller develops within the hole formed, which spirals around the side of the pier. In plan, the vortex system has a horseshoe shape and is frequently referred to as a horseshoe vortex (Fig. 6).

The scour hole will increase in size until an equilibrium depth is reached. The equilibrium depth is dependent on which of the following scour conditions prevail.

(*a*) Clear water scour, where bed movement occurs only adjacent to the piers. The equilibrium depth is reached when the shear stresses at the surface of the scour hole are insufficient to eject particles.

(*b*) Sediment transporting scour, where the whole river bed is in motion. The equilibrium depth is reached when the amount of sediment entering the scour hole is balanced by the amount leaving.

The depth at which the equilibrium condition is reached will be greatest at the transition between the clear water and sediment transporting conditions, i.e. at the threshold of movement, when the approach velocity equals U_c, the average critical velocity for initiating sediment movement (Fig. 7 after Chabert and Engeldinger[9]). To determine whether clear

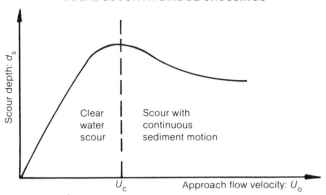

Fig. 7. Scour depth against approach velocity (after Chabert and Engeldinger[9])

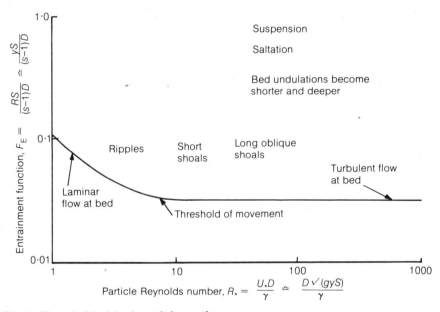

Fig. 8. Threshold of bed particle motion

water or sediment transporting conditions prevail, reference can be made to Fig. 8. This shows the relationship between the particle entrainment function and particle Reynolds number, which was originally derived by Shields and subsequently modified by Ackers and White.[1] Clear water conditions are defined by points lying below the line and sediment transporting conditions by points above. The line represents the threshold of movement. The entrainment function F_E is given by the following relationship (for notation see Fig. 8).

35

$$F_E = RS(s-1)^{-1}D^{-1} \tag{22}$$

For wide channels, this relationship approximates to

$$F_E = yS(s-1)^{-1}D^{-1} \tag{22a}$$

The particle Reynolds number, R_*, is given by

$$R_* = \frac{U_*D}{\nu} \tag{23}$$

which, for wide channels, approximates to

$$R_* = \frac{D\sqrt{(gyS)}}{\nu} \tag{23a}$$

Estimating local scour at a cylindrical pier

The interaction of the flow around a bridge pier and the river bed surrounding it is very complex. The subject has attracted the interest of many researchers who have used empirical methods or a combination of analytical and empirical techniques to fit their equations for scour prediction to the available experimental and field data. The research, however, has concentrated on scour effects in cohesionless material and there is no guidance in the literature for estimating local scour depth in cohesive materials.

Local scour in cohesionless material

A review of the numerous equations which have been developed to predict the depth of scour in cohesionless materials adjacent to a cylindrical pier is contained in references 18 and 25. For practical purposes appropriate equations may be selected from Equations (24)–(31) according to Table 8.

$$d_s = 1 \cdot 17 U_o^{0 \cdot 62} b^{0 \cdot 62} \text{ (Shen I[28])} \tag{24}$$
$$d_s = 1 \cdot 59 U_o^{0 \cdot 67} b^{0 \cdot 67} \text{ (Shen II[28])} \tag{25}$$
$$d_s = 1 \cdot 11 y_o^{0 \cdot 5} b^{0 \cdot 5} \text{ (Laursen[22])} \tag{26}$$
$$d_s = 1 \cdot 8 y_o^{0 \cdot 75} b^{0 \cdot 25} - y_o \text{ (Blench[6])} \tag{27}$$
$$d_s = C y_o \text{ (regime equation)} \tag{28}$$

where $0 \cdot 5 < C < 1 \cdot 0$

$$y_o = 0 \cdot 38 q_o^{0 \cdot 67} D_{50}^{-0 \cdot 17} \text{ (Blench[6])} \tag{29}$$
$$y_o = 0 \cdot 47 q_o^{0 \cdot 8} D_{90}^{-0 \cdot 12} \text{ (Kellerhals[19])} \tag{30}$$
$$y_o = 0 \cdot 23(s-1)^{-0 \cdot 43} q_o^{0 \cdot 86} D_{90}^{-0 \cdot 29} \tag{31}$$

In the above equations d_s is the depth of scour measured below upstream bed level, m; b is the width of pier, m; U_o is the approach flow velocity, m/s; y_o is the depth upstream of pier, m; q_o is the discharge per unit width

Table 8. Équations for predicting local scour at cylindrical piers in cohesionless materials*

Scour condition	Sand or gravel bed	F = Froude number $= \dfrac{U}{\sqrt{(g\,y)}}$	D_{50}	Equation
Clear water	Sand	—	—	Equation (24)
Sediment transporting	Sand	$F < 0.5$	—	Equation (26)
		$F > 0.5$	—	The larger value given by Equation (25) or (26)
		$F < 0.3$	$0.001 < D_{50} < 0.004$	Equations (27) and (29) or Equations (28) and (29)
Clear water	Gravel	—	—	Equations (28) and (31)
Sediment transporting	Gravel	—	—	Equations (28) and (30)

*In cases where the Froude number exceeds 0.8, a model investigation to determine scour effects is recommended.

37

Table 9. Depth of scour at piers in cohesive soils (b = width of pier)

Pier shape in plan	Inclination of pier faces	Depth of scour
Circle	Vertical	$1 \cdot 5\,b$
Rectangle	Vertical	$2 \cdot 0\,b$
Lenticular	Vertical	$1 \cdot 2\,b$
Rectangle with semicircular noses	Vertical	$1 \cdot 5\,b$
Rectangle with semicircular noses	Inclined inwards towards top. Angle more than 20° to vertical	$1 \cdot 0\,b$
Rectangle with semicircular noses	Inclined outwards towards top. Angle more than 20° to vertical	$2 \cdot 0\,b$

upstream of pier, m²/s; D_{50} is the median particle size of bed material, m; D_{90} is the size of bed material such that 90% of the particles by number is smaller, m; s is the specific gravity of the bed material.

Equation (28) simply states that scour depth is between half and full regime depth. Equations (29)−(31) are equations for determining regime depth depending on river conditions. Equation (31) has been derived directly from the threshold of motion relationships defined in Fig. 8. Use of the procedure for calculating scour depths is illustrated by an example given below in the section 'Estimating local scour at non-cylindrical piers'.

Local scour in cohesive material

There are very few reference data on scour in cohesive soils or on the effect of the degree of consolidation on resistance to scour. Until more reliable information is available, therefore, it is recommended that simple formulae based on pier width be used to estimate scour in cohesive soils. Table 9, which is based on data in reference 26, may be used as a guide.

Estimating local scour at non-cylindrical piers

Estimation of local scour at non-cylindrical piers may be obtained by applying suitable factors to the equations for predicting scour around cylindrical piers given above in the section 'Estimating local scour at a cylindrical pier'.

Non-cylindrical piers may be designed to present a sharper nose to the oncoming flow than cylindrical piers. This will have the effect of reducing the strength of the horseshoe vortex and hence the depth of scour. For piers designed with blunter noses the converse is true. Factors for adjusting for non-cylindrical shapes are given in Table 10 and are referred to as f_2 factors.

Scour at non-cylindrical piers will vary with the direction of the oncoming flow, or angle of attack. Factors, referred to as f_3 factors, which may be used for adjusting for oblique flow, are given in Fig. 9. Hence, for non-cylindrical piers in oblique flow, the local scour may be estimated from

$$\text{scour depth} = d_s f_2 f_3 \tag{32}$$

where d_s is the scour depth at a cylindrical pier calculated from the appropriate equations selected from Equations (24)–(31), f_2 is the factor to account for pier shape, f_3 is the factor to account for oblique flow.

The following example is given to illustrate the procedure for calculating scour depth. The field data are taken from reference 8 and are for the Tuakau Bridge, New Zealand.

Depth of upstream flow: $y_o = 3$ m
Approach velocity: $U_o = 0·87$ m/s
Median particle size: $D_{50} = 0·78$ mm
Pier length, width: $L = 8·85$ m, $b = 2·44$ m
Froude number $= U_o/\sqrt{(gy_o)} = 0·16$
Critical approach velocity $= 0·3$ m/s

Table 10. Pier shape factor, f_2

Shape in plan	$\dfrac{\text{Length}}{\text{Width}}$	f_2	Reference
Circular	1·0	1·0	—
Lenticular	2·0	0·91	23
	3·0	0·76	23
	4·0	0·67	30
		0·73	9
	7·0	0·41	30
Parabolic nose		0·8	26
Triangular 60°		0·75	31
90°		1·25	31
Elliptic	2·0	0·91	23
	3·0	0·83	23
Ogival	4·0	0·86	30
		0·92	9
Rectangular	2·0	1·11	23
	4·0	1·40✔	30
	6·0	1·11	23

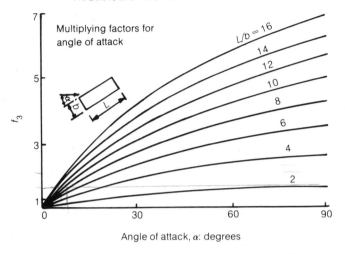

Fig. 9. Variation of f_3 with angle of attack α (after Laursen[22])

Measured scour $= 2\cdot75$ m
Angle of attack $= 10°$
Factor to account for pier shape: $f_2 = 1\cdot11$
Factor to account for oblique flow: $f_3 = 1\cdot3$.

This river can be classified as a sand bed river and since the entrainment function computed from Equation (22a) is greater than $0\cdot1$, it is evident from Fig. 8 that sediment transporting conditions prevail. Referring to Table 6, it is appropriate to use Equation (26) to estimate scour depth. Substituting Equation (26) into Equation (32) yields the following equation for scour depth, in metres

$$\begin{aligned}
\text{scour depth} &= 1\cdot11 y_0^{0\cdot5} b^{0\cdot5} f_2 f_3 \\
&= 1\cdot11 \times 1\cdot73 \times 1\cdot56 \times 1\cdot11 \times 1\cdot3 \\
&= 4\cdot3
\end{aligned}$$

Hence, the estimated scour depth is $4\cdot3$ m compared with a measured value of $2\cdot75$ m. The estimate may be better than is apparent from the comparison, since it was noted by the observers[8] that, in view of the limited number of depth observations taken, the scour depth could have been greater.

Estimating local scour at pile groups

Bridge piers are commonly founded on groups of piles. The pile cap will be at or above the general scour level and will generally be of larger plan dimensions than the pier. The flow pattern for this situation will therefore be different in two ways from that for a plain cylindrical pier described above in the section, 'Mechanism of scour'. First, the downward component of flow at the pier nose will be deflected horizontally at the pile cap so tending to prevent the formation of the horseshoe vortex; secondly, a complicated flow pattern will be set up within the pile group. Limited research has been conducted into the scour around pile groups[15] but, as yet, no generalised guidelines can be formulated. In the meantime, a conservative estimate may be obtained by assuming that the group effectively becomes a single solid pier of the dimensions formed by the outermost piles in the group.

Rate of scour

As it is not possible at present to formulate general guidelines for estimating the rate at which local scour will take place in either cohesionless or cohesive soils, it is recommended that, for the time being, the calculated maximum equilibrium depth of local scour be assumed in all cases. This approach is obviously more conservative in the design of temporary as opposed to permanent works, particularly in cohesive soils.

Local scour at abutments and training works

Abutments and training works can be subjected to a wide range of approach flow conditions of varying complexity, which complicate any attempt to produce generalised guidelines for estimating scour. In any given design situation it is therefore recommended that scour depths should be estimated either from data collected at similar river works in the same locality or from a model investigation.

An estimate of scour may be obtained by first estimating the general scour level; this may be taken as the bed level corresponding to the mean depth of flow calculated from the appropriate equations quoted in Chapter 1. To then obtain the maximum depth, the mean depth is factored by a multiplier selected from Table 11 (reference 6). Strictly, the multipliers apply to sand bed rivers but, for approximate indications, they may be applied to gravel and cohesive bed rivers.

In the case of 'spill-through' abutments with revetments, the scoured level may be obtained by applying the appropriate multiplier for banks to the general scour level for the waterway. In the case of abutments

Table 11. Multipliers for estimating scour depth at abutments and training works

Nature of location	Multiplier
Nose of groynes or guidebanks	2·0 to 2·75
Flow impinging at right angles on bank	2·25
Flow parallel to bank	1·5 to 2·0

which protrude into the river flow, it is more difficult to give design guidelines. A conservative approach would be to assume the scoured level to be the lower of the scour level estimated for the piers and the level calculated by factoring the general scour level with a multiplier of $2 \cdot 25$, a multiplier suggested in reference 16 for applying to river locations adjacent to walls.

References

1. Ackers, P. and White, W.R. Sediment transport—new approach and analysis. *Proc. Am. Soc. Civ. Engrs*, 1973, **99**, No. HY11, Nov., 1973.
2. Ahmad, M. Discussion of 'Scour at bridge crossings' (by E.M. Laursen). *Trans. Am. Soc. Civ. Engrs*, Part 1, 1962, **127**, 198–206.
3. Arunachalam, K. Scour around bridge piers. *J. Indian Roads Congress*, Paper No. 251, 1965.
4. Baker, C.J. New design equations for scour around bridge piers. *Proc. Am. Soc. Civ. Engrs*, 1981, **107**, No. HY4, Apr.
5. Bata, C. *Erozija oko novosadskog mostovskog stuba* (Serbian). (Scour around bridge piers), Institut za Vodoprivredu, Jaroslav Cerni Beograd, Yugoslavia, 1960. English translation by Markovic filed at Colorado State University, Civil Engineering Department, Fort Collins.
6. Blench, T. *Mobile bed fluviology*, University of Alberta Press, Edmonton, 1969.
7. Breusers, H.N.C. Scour around drilling platforms. *Bull. Hydr. Res.*, IAHR, 1965, **19**, 276.
8. Breusers, H.N.C. *et al.* Local scour around cylindrical piers. *J. Hydr. Res.*, IAHR, 1977, **15**, No. 3, 211–252.
9. Chabert, J. and Engeldinger, P. *Etude des affouillements autour des piles des ponts*, Laboratoire National d'Hydraulique, Chatou, 1956.
10. Chitale, S.V. Discussion of 'Scour at bridge crossings' (by E.M. Laursen). *Trans. Am. Soc. Civ. Engrs*, Part 1, 1962, **127**, 191–196.
11. Federal Highway Administration. Stream channel degradation and aggradation: analysis of impacts to highway crossings. *Report No. FHWA/RD–80/159*, Dept of Transportation, USA, March 1981.
12. Federal Highway Administration. Methods of assessment of stream related hazards to highways and bridges. *Report No. FHWA/RD– 80/160*, Dept of Transportation, USA, March 1981.
13. Garde, R.J. Local bed variation at bridge piers in alluvial channels. *University of Roorke Research Journal 1961*, **IV**, 1961 (India).
14. Hancu, S. Sur le calcul des affouillements locaux dans la zone des piles du pont. *Proc. 14th Congress IAHR*, 1971, **3**, 299–306.
15. Hannah, C.R. *Scour at pile groups*, ME thesis, University of Canterbury, Christchurch, New Zealand, 1978.
16. Indian Roads Congress. *Standard specifications and codes of practice for bridges*, 1966.
17. Inglis, C.C. The behaviour and control of rivers and canals. *Research Publication No. 13*, Part 2, Central Power, Irrigation and Navigation Report, Poona Research Station, India, 1949.

18. Jain, S.C. Maximum clear-water scour around circular piers. *Proc. Am. Soc. Civ. Engrs*, 1981, **107**, No. HY5, May.
19. Kellerhals, R. Stable channels with gravel paved beds. *Proc. Am. Soc. Civ. Engrs*, 1967, **93**, No. WW1, Feb., 63.
20. Knezevic, B. *Prilog proucavanju erozije oko mostoviskih stubova* (Serbian). (Contributions to research work of erosion around bridge piers), Institut za Vodoprivredu, Jaroslav Cerni Beograd, Yugoslavia, 1960. English translation by Markovic filed at Colorado State University, Civil Engineering Department, Fort Collins.
21. Larras, J. Profondeurs maximales d'erosion des fonds mobiles autour des piles en rivière. *Annales des Ponts et Chausses*, 1963, **133**, No. 4, 411–424.
22. Laursen, E.M. Scour at bridge crossings. *Bulletin No. 8*, Iowa Highway Research Board, 1958.
23. Laursen, E.M. and Toch, A. Scour around bridge piers and abutments. *Bulletin No. 4*, Iowa Highway Research Board, 1956.
24. Maza Alvarex, J.A. *Scour in river beds*, Instituto de Ingenieria, Universidad Nacional Autonoma de Mexico, Ciudad Universitaria, Mexico, 1977.
25. Melville, B.W. Scour at bridge sites. *Report No. 104*, University of Auckland, School of Engineering, Auckland, New Zealand.
26. Neill, C.R. *Guide to bridge hydraulics*, Roads and Transportation Association of Canada, University of Toronto Press, 1973.
27. Qadar, A. The vortex scour mechanism at bridge piers. *Proc. Instn Civ. Engrs*, Part 2, 1981, **71**, Sept., 739–757.
28. Shen, H.W. *et al*. Local scour around bridge piers. *Proc. Am. Soc. Civ. Engrs, J. of Hydraulics Divn*, 1969, **95**, No. HY6,
29. Thomas, A.R. Discussions of 'Scour at bridge crossings' (by E.M. Laursen). *Trans. Am. Soc. Civ. Engrs*, Part 1, 1962, **127**, 196–198.
30. Tison, L.J. Erosion autour de piles de ponts en rivière. *Annales des Travaux Publics de Belgique*, 1940, **41**, No. 6.
31. Venkatodri, C. *et al*. Scour around bridge piers and abutments. *J. Irrigation and Power*, 1965, Jan.,

Chapter 6

Forces on bridge piers

Introduction

This chapter discusses the forces which require consideration in the design of bridge piers. These forces arise from hydrodynamic loading, debris and ship impact, and in cold climates, from ice.

Hydrodynamic forces

A river flowing past a bridge pier will exert a hydrodynamic force on the pier, the component of which in the direction of flow is known as drag and the component normal to the flow as lift. In fully turbulent flow, the force is generated from a combination of the shear stress against the pier face and the pressure differential caused by flow separation at the pier tail.

Drag and lift forces which are generally small compared with other forces may be determined for the shapes shown in Fig. 10 using the procedure proposed by Apelt and Isaacs[1] from the relationships

$$\text{drag force (N), } F_D = C_D \rho U_o^2 y_o L / 2 \tag{33}$$

$$\text{lift force (N), } F_L = C_L \rho U_o^2 y_o L / 2 \tag{34}$$

in which U_o is the approach flow velocity, m/s; y_o is the depth upstream of pier, m; L is the length of pier, m (or pier diameter for a single cylindrical pier) (see Fig. 10); ρ is the water density, kg/m^3; C_D is the drag coefficient; C_L is the lift coefficient.

Definite relationships for the evaluation of drag and lift coefficients cannot be determined so, where accurate estimates are required, model studies are necessary.

However, preliminary estimates of the coefficients for cylindrical piers may be obtained from Table 12 and for pier configurations 2, 3 and 4 illustrated in Fig. 10, from charts derived by Apelt and Isaacs[1] which are given in Appendix A. When the coefficients are substituted into Equations

44

FORCES ON BRIDGE PIERS

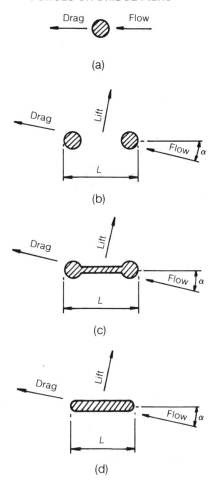

Fig. 10. Definition sketch of pier cross-sectional shapes: (a) type 1, cylindrical; (b) 2, twin cylinder; (c) 3, dumb-bell; (d) 4, plate

(33) and (34), drag and lift forces may be obtained which must be assumed to act at mid-depth. This approximate analysis will enable the designer to determine whether the hydrodynamic forces are significant and if a model study is necessary.

An illustration of the use of the charts is given below. Drag and lift forces are calculated for the Exe Bridge piers, Exeter, UK, and compared with those predicted by a model study.[5]

For the Exe Bridge, $U_o = 2 \cdot 7$ m/s, $y_o = 6 \cdot 35$ m, $L = 22 \cdot 75$ m, $b = 1 \cdot 3$ m, and $\alpha = 19°$.

The pier is classified as type 4. Thus using the charts given in Appendix A, $C_D = 0 \cdot 4$, $C_L = 0 \cdot 8$.

Table 12. Drag coefficients for cylindrical piers (after Rouse[13])*

Ratio of pier height to diameter	Reynolds number	Coefficient of drag, C_D
1	10^5	0·63
5	10^5	0·74
20	10^5	0·90
	10^5	1·20
5	$> 5 \times 10^5$	0·35
∞	5×10^5	0·33

*Reynolds number $= U_o b/\nu$ where U_o = approach flow velocity, m/s; b = pier diameter, m; ν = kinematic viscosity, m²/s.

Hence

$$F_D = C_D \rho U_o^2 y_o L/2$$
$$= (0·4 \times 1000 \times 2·7^2 \times 6·35 \times 22·75/2) \text{ N}$$
$$= 210 \text{ kN}$$

$$F_L = C_L \rho U_o^2 y_o L/2$$
$$= (0·8) \times 1000 \times 2·7^2 \times 6·35 \times 22·75/2) \text{ N}$$
$$= 420 \text{ kN}$$

Resolving the drag and lift forces parallel and normal to the axis of the piers, the forces are 62 kN and 465 kN respectively, which compare with 40 kN and 330 kN predicted by the model. The forces in the model were found to act at between 0·53 and 0·62 times the depth of flow, measured from the bed. In magnitude, the forces predicted by the model are less than the forces calculated using the charts of Apelt and Isaacs,[1] but better agreement might be expected in cases where the ratio of pier length to width agrees more closely with that of the piers used in the derivation of the charts. With respect to the line of action of the forces, it is apparent that in this example, the assumption that forces are acting at mid-depth is reasonable.

Ice forces

Ice is a highly anisotropic and heterogeneous material, exhibiting such complex visco-elastic behaviour that analytical methods for assessing forces generated by the interaction of ice and structures rely heavily on both full-scale measurements and small-scale experimental work.

For inland river structures, the critical mode of ice action is most likely to be the impact of large ice sheets with piers or piles at ice break-up. In the case of vertical piers, the ice fails by crushing around the contact perimeter, although small ice sheets may fail by splitting. In the case of inclined piers, when the ice sheets may ride up the pier face, the critical failure mode may be either one of crushing, shearing or bending.

Formulae have been proposed by Korzhavin[6] for predicting horizontal ice forces resulting from crushing, shearing and bending failure modes, but difficulties arise in the selection of the right values for the empirical coefficients and ice strengths in each mode when applying the formulae to practical cases.

Simpler approaches are suggested in Canadian and Soviet Design Codes.[2,14] A sample calculation based on the Canadian Code is given below to illustrate the order of magnitude of ice forces. Parameter values extracted from the Code are given in Appendix B.

The horizontal force F_H, kN, may be obtained from the following equation

$$F_H = C_n p \, t_i \, b \tag{35}$$

where C_n is the coefficient for nose inclination; p is the effective ice strength, kN/m²; t_i is the thickness of ice in contact, m; b is the width of pier, m.

Example

Using the hypothetical data below and the Canadian Code (see Appendix B), the ice force on a bridge pier is calculated as $C_n = 1 \cdot 0$ (pier has inclination $<15°$), $p = 1380$ kN/m², $t_i = 0 \cdot 75$ m and $b = 1 \cdot 5$ m. Hence

$$\begin{aligned} F_H &= C_n p \, t_i \, b \\ &= 1 \cdot 0 \times 1380 \times 0 \cdot 75 \times 1 \cdot 5 \\ &= 1553 \text{ kN} \end{aligned}$$

Debris forces

Debris loading on piers may take one of two forms

(a) impact forces resulting from debris colliding with the piers
(b) hydrodynamic forces on trapped debris being transferred to the pier.

In respect of impact forces, the Australian Highway Bridge Design Specification[10] recommends that the designer should allow for a force equivalent to that exerted by a 2 t log, travelling at the normal stream velocity and arrested within distances of 150 mm and 75 mm for column-type and solid-type concrete piers respectively. Current practice within some UK consultancy firms is to allow for a force exerted by a 10 t mass, travelling at the design streamflow velocity, which is arrested in a distance of 75 mm.

47

In respect of additional hydrodynamic forces, an allowance for the hydrodynamic force exerted on a minimum depth of $1 \cdot 2$ m of debris is recommended in reference 10. The length of debris jam to be applied to a pier should be half of the sum of the adjacent spans up to a maximum of 21 m. The formula below is given in reference 4 to calculate the pressure due to the trapped debris:

$$P_d = 0 \cdot 517 \, U_o^2 \tag{36}$$

where P_d = pressure, kN/m^2; U_o = approach velocity, m/s.

In cases where this type of debris blockage is considered applicable, the increase in the flow velocity beneath the debris and the consequent increased scour must be considered.

It should be noted, however, that where a bridge pier is protected by an independent fender system, it may be unnecessary to design for debris forces on the pier and that, usually, impact and hydrodynamic forces due to debris are not considered to be applied concurrently.

Impact forces due to ship collision

Ship to bridge collision has become of increasing concern in the past decade because of a growing number of serious accidents. The following factors may be considered as the most likely causes of collision.

(*a*) *Mechanical failure:* this may be due to engine failure, but is more frequently due to steering failure or reduced steering ability.

(*b*) *Human error:* this may be made by the helmsman, engine room crew or pilot.

(*c*) *Currents and wind squalls:* these can be important factors, particularly when a vessel has to turn on to a short approach to proceed through a narrow navigation span.

(*d*) *Width of navigation span:* the minimum desirable width is dependent on such factors as traffic density, periods of reduced visibility, length of straight approach, currents, navigable width of waterway, and widths and lengths of ships passing through. It has been suggested[11] that minimum navigation span sizes should be $1 \cdot 5 - 2$ times the length of typical vessels passing through the bridge.

(*e*) *Fog or poor visibility:* this causes difficulty in judging speed and distances in relation to bridge piers and other vessels. Ship's radar will only be of use in passing safely under a bridge if the navigation channel is marked by radar-reflective buoys.

The risk of collision may be reduced, for example, by introducing radar-reflective buoys to mark the approach channel, by providing bridge lighting and by restricting movements when adverse conditions prevail, but an element of collision risk will always remain. The designer is therefore faced with the problem of assessing the probability of various types of collision, deciding on an acceptable level of risk in both economic and human life terms, evaluating the impact forces due to the ship collision and then either designing the bridge structure to absorb the collision force, or designing an appropriate independent protection system for the piers.

Assessing the probability of ship collision

The assessment of the probability of ship collision with bridge piers is complicated by the many factors involved and made more difficult by the relatively few statistics available. Three methods have been suggested in reference 7.

(a) *Historical approach.* Collision statistics at other bridges are used to determine apparent frequencies at these bridges. These data may then be used as a guide to collision frequency at the proposed bridge. A model of this situation can be represented by

$$A_c = R_c T_c \tag{37}$$

where A_c is the number of collisions per year, R_c is the risk factor combining the risks associated with the various causes of collision referred to earlier, T_c is the traffic in ship transits through the bridge each year.

The successful application of this method relies on obtaining data for a large number of situations and equating the risk factors obtained with those of the proposed bridge.

(b) *Statistical approach.* This method is based on a model of the form

total probability = (causation probability × geometric factor)
of collision

The causation probability is defined as the probability of an accident resulting from such factors as engine failure, poor visibility, etc. Data from around the world for ship-to-ship collisions, ship strandings and groundings and ship-to-fixed-object collisions have been used to determine causation probabilities for each factor.[4,8] Causation probabilities for the factors which are considered likely to result in collisions at the proposed bridge are then assessed and summed to give the cumulative causation probability. The geometric factor is the probability of an out-of-control ship colliding with a bridge pier. Two methods for assessing the geometric factor are given in references 4 and 8.

(c) *Empirical approach.* This method uses information on ship-to-bridge collisions throughout the world, and relies on the advice of maritime experts in interpreting the factors causing the collisions, and in assessing the probability of collisions occurring at the proposed bridge due to similar factors.

By application of one or more of these approaches, the expected frequency of a ship-to-bridge collision with respect to the number of ship transits through the bridge may be obtained. When multiplied by the annual number of ship transits, the return period in years is obtained.

The question of the level of risk which should be accepted in any given situation remains unanswered. It is clear that the cost of safeguarding the bridge piers against ship impact forces will increase for reducing levels of risk and that at some level, which will vary from situation to situation, the additional cost of safeguarding the bridge piers will be considered unjustified when compared with the loss from a possible collision. However, this level is not easily defined, particularly since loss of human life may be involved. Risk levels have been considered in a study of a bridge crossing in Denmark,[3] and the resulting design proposals were for a collision risk of once in 10 000 years.

Assessing the magnitude of impact forces

When a ship collides with a bridge pier, its kinetic energy is absorbed by deflection of the pier and by crushing of the ship's bow or hull plates. The amount of energy absorbed by the pier is small since the lateral movement of the pier to the point of collapse is relatively small. In assessing impact forces it is therefore reasonable to assume that all the kinetic energy is absorbed by crushing at the ship's bow or hull.

Minorsky[9] has related in equation form the energy absorbed in ship-to-ship collisions with the volume of steel deformed at the collision point. His equation was modified by Woisin and Gerlach[16] for the case of a ship colliding head on with a rigid structure, such as a bridge pier, to

$$E = 47\,000\,R_s \tag{38}$$

where E = energy absorbed on ship impact, kNm; R_s = volume of deformed steel, m³.

The energy which must be absorbed on impact is also given by

$$E = \tfrac{1}{2}k\Delta V^2 \tag{39}$$

where Δ = ship's displacement, t; V = ship's velocity, m/s; k = hydrodynamic supplementary mass coefficient. Substituting (39) into (38) enables a solution for R_s to be obtained. By the method indicated in Appendix C, the value for R_s may be converted for any given bow construction into a depth of damage penetration. Depending on the depth of damage penetration compared with the ship's beam, the average impact force is then given by

$$\text{average impact force, kN} = \frac{k\Delta V^2}{2P_i} \text{ for } P_i > J \tag{40}$$

or

$$\text{average impact force, kN} = \frac{k\Delta V^2}{2P_i} \sqrt{\left(\frac{P_i}{J}\right)} \text{ for } P_i < J \tag{41}$$

where P_i = depth of damage penetration, m; J = ship's beam, m.

Model investigations reported in reference 16 have shown that for a brief period $(0 \cdot 1 - 0 \cdot 2 \text{ s})$ the impact force can be twice the average value. The case of impact resulting from side-on ship collision is dealt with in reference 15.

Protection of bridge piers from ship collision

Protection systems for piers fall into two main categories: type (i) systems which depend upon the development of high impact forces and which use the crushing of the bow of a colliding vessel to absorb the energy of motion, and type (ii) methods which rely on absorbing a ship's energy within the protection system.

Type (i) systems may be divided into

(a) gravity systems: these may consist of groups of large-diameter piles strapped together and situated in front of the bridge pile caps. Such methods become prohibitively expensive in deep water and for protecting multi-span bridges.

(b) floating concrete pontoons: although these pontoons are anchored to the bed of the river, they rely largely on their mass to resist local impact forces. Again they become very expensive when there are a large number of piers to protect.

Type (ii) systems may be divided into

(a) rock embankments
(b) fender systems
(c) river-bed and river-surface arrester systems.

A rock embankment or island protection to individual piers is a method which is often used successfully particularly in shallow-water conditions. In deeper water a continuous rock embankment, with a break for the navigation channel, is necessary both upstream and downstream of the bridge. However, such embankments may cause serious changes to the river regime and detailed study would be required before such a method could be selected.

Any type of fender system which is attached directly to the bridge piers, such as gravity, rubber-type, torsion pin, steel cellular and rubber cellular

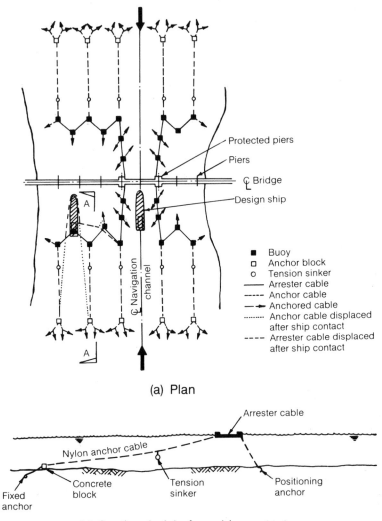

(a) Plan

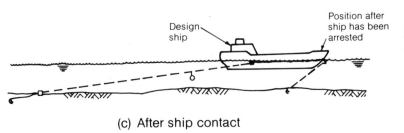

(b) Section A–A before ship contact

(c) After ship contact

Fig. 11. Typical cable arrester system

fenders, requires the pier to withstand considerable horizontal forces and is therefore not practicable for waterways on which large vessels travel. The most effective independently supported fenders rely on the ductility of concrete in the plastic range to absorb energy. This means that much larger amounts of energy can be absorbed than is possible with a recoverable fender system.

A vertical-piled fender system consists of large-diameter vertical piles rock anchored to the bed. The piles are fixed at the top by a rigid fender beam so that each pile forms two plastic hinges to absorb energy. It should be noted that it would be necessary to replace the protection system at a particular pier on each occasion that a major ship collision occurred.

A tension beam fender system consists of reinforced concrete fender beams which are restrained by piled dolphins. The fender beams are set in the form of a V so that an errant ship is directed into the apex. The energy of motion is absorbed by structural reinforcing bars which are not bonded to the concrete beams, but welded into a continuous length along the beams.

There are two types of arrester cable system. The first type comprises cables and anchors laid across the bed of the river, and relies on the errant vessel lowering its anchors and dragging them along the bed until a fluke catches an arrester cable. The arrester anchors are then dragged along the river bed and gradually bring the ship to rest. This method is not entirely satisfactory since it depends on a number of variables associated with the ship, i.e. the strength and condition of the ship's cable, the ability of the anchor flukes to grip the cable, and the effectiveness of the ship's winch brakes.

The second type has a cable system located on the surface of the river. Such a system is outlined in Fig. 11 and consists of a buoyed cable extending over the length of the bridge. Energy-absorbing cables secure the arrester cable back to fixed anchor clumps, and a tension cable and sinker system holds the cable in position against winds and currents. An errant vessel picks up the cable across its bow and carries it forward until the slack is taken up after which deceleration begins as the anchor cables stretch. The system is designed to absorb completely the energy of the vessel.

References

1. Apelt, C.J. and Isaacs, L.T. Bridge piers—hydrodynamic force coefficients. *Proc. Am. Soc. Civ. Engrs, J. of Hydraulics Divn*, 1968, Jan.
2. Canadian Standards Association. Design of highway bridges. *National Standard of Canada CAN 3-56-M78*, Rexdale, Ontario, 1978.
3. Frandsen, A.G. and Lango, H. Ship collision problems, I Great Belt Bridge, II International Enquiry. *IABSE Proceedings*, 1980, May, 31–80.

4. Fujii, Y. *et al*. The probability of stranding. *J. Navigation*, 1974.

5. Hydraulics Research Station. Exe Bridges, Exeter—model investigation of forces on bridge piers, HRS, Wallingford, July 1966.

6. Korzhavin, K.N. *Action of ice on engineering structures*, USSR Academy of Science, Siberian Branch. Draft translation by Cold Regional Research Engineering Laboratory, 1971.

7. Maunsell & Partners Pty. *Tasman Bridge—risk of ship collision and methods of protection*, September 1978.

8. Macduff, T. The probability of vessel collisions. *Ocean Industry*, 1974, Sept.

9. Minorsky, V.U. An analysis of ship collisions with reference to protection of nuclear power plants. *J. Ship Res.*, 1959, Oct.

10. National Association of Australian State Road Authorities. *Highway bridge design specification*, 1965.

11. Ostenfield, Chr. Ship collisions against bridge piers. *IABSE Mémoires*, 1965.

12. Roads and Transportation Association of Canada. *Ice effects on bridges*, 1981.

13. Rouse, H. *Engineering hydraulics*, John Wiley, 1950.

14. State Committee of the Council of Ministers for Construction (G. Osstroi, USSR). Instructions for determining ice loads on river structures, *Standard SN 76–66*. NRCC Tech. Translation, 1973.

15. Saul, R. and Svensson, H. On the theory of ship collision against bridge piers. *IABSE Periodica, Proceeding P-51/82*, 1982.

16. Woisin, G. and Gerlach, W. On the estimation of forces developed between ships and offshore structures. *8th AISM/IALA int. conf. on lighthouses and other aids to navigation*, Stockholm, Paper 1.1.9, 1970.

Chapter 7

Bank protection and river training

Introduction

Earlier sections have described how scour can occur around bridge piers and abutments, and methods have been presented for calculating the magnitude of this scour. It has also been shown how bridge approach embankments in meandering channels can be endangered by the migration of the channel. This chapter describes the methods commonly adopted to protect piers and abutments from scour, and also looks at methods of controlling the approach channel to the bridge. The ensuing sections are intended only as an introduction to the subject and, for more rigorous treatments, the reader is referred to the references in this chapter.

Protection of foundations against scour

The designer has the choice of designing bridge foundations in rivers to be adequately supported below the lowest estimated level of scour, or of designing suitable protection works, such as a rock apron, which will limit the depth of scour and permit design for support below the level of the protection works. An example of a typical foundation is illustrated in Fig. 12 in which a rock apron limits the depth of scour to the general scour level, the level at which protection is usually provided.

In the case of rock apron design a model investigation may be appropriate to determine the size of stone and the extent of the apron. Otherwise design may be based on experience of similar installations in the same locality or from theoretical considerations. Neill[10] recommends that the apron should be laid below the general scour level, that it should project around the nose of the pier by $1 \cdot 5$ times pier width, and that it should be equal in thickness to twice the D_{50} size of stone (D_{50} = median particle size of rip rap stone). Gales[5] has recommended wedge-shaped pitching in plan around piers as illustrated in Fig. 13. This is a more conservative solution than that proposed by Neill but some economy could probably be achieved by reducing the quantity of stone pitching at the tail of the pier where scour conditions are less severe than at the nose.

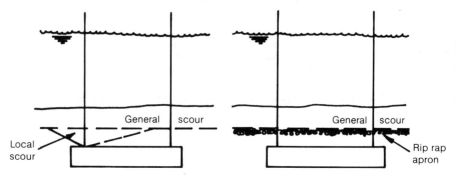

Fig. 12. Protection to pier foundations

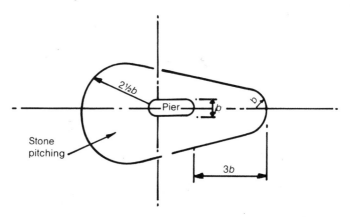

Fig. 13. Dimensions of pier protection recommended by Gales[5]

Protection of river banks

Ideally a bridge crossing would be located in a stable reach of river channel, but in many cases it will not be practicable or economical to do so. In such cases adequate measures must be taken to control the approach channel to prevent bank erosion and migrating meanders endangering the bridge construction. General descriptions of methods commonly adopted in bank protection and river training works are given below.

Bank and slope revetment

In selecting the most appropriate type of revetment, the degree of protection afforded, environmental acceptance, ease of installation, ease of maintenance, expected life and cost must be taken into consideration. Some of the types of revetment commonly used are stone rip rap, steel sheet piling, gabions, precast concrete blocks and in situ concrete. For a detailed analysis of protection systems, see references 6 and 7. Since rip rap protection has particular application in river bank protection and also in the protection of groynes and guide banks, which are discussed later, a more detailed treatment is given here.

Rip rap design

A number of formulae[2,4,8,11,15] are available to determine the size of stone required for rip rap. The method proposed by Maynord[9] has been selected for consideration here, after a comparison with other methods had shown it to be relatively easy to apply and to have the facility of introducing a factor of safety into the design. The basic equation for rip rap design is

$$\frac{D_{50}}{y_o} = C \, F^3 \tag{42}$$

where D_{50} is the median particle size of rip rap stone, m; y_o is the depth upstream of bank, m; F is the Froude number $= U_o/\sqrt{(gy_o)}$; U_o is the approach velocity, m/s; C is the coefficient determined from laboratory and field testing, appropriate values for which may be selected from Table 13.

It is suggested that for river works, the mean channel flow velocity is factored by the multipliers given in Table 14 to give maximum approach flow velocity.

An example to illustrate the use of this method is as follows.

Data: $y_o = 3 \cdot 0$ m
$U_o = 4$ m/s
Location: straight reach

For protection around a bridge pier use a factor of safety of 2. Thus assuming a flat bed, $C = 0 \cdot 28$ and for a straight reach the mean channel flow should be factored by $1 \cdot 25$.

Table 13. Coefficients for rip rap design (after Maynord[9])

Slope	Factor of safety	Coefficient C
Flat	$1 \cdot 0$	$0 \cdot 22$
Flat	$1 \cdot 5$	$0 \cdot 25$
Flat	$2 \cdot 0$	$0 \cdot 28$
1:3 or less	$1 \cdot 0$	$0 \cdot 22$
1:3 or less	$1 \cdot 5$	$0 \cdot 25$
1:3 or less	$2 \cdot 0$	$0 \cdot 28$
1:2	$1 \cdot 0$	$0 \cdot 26$
1:2	$1 \cdot 5$	$0 \cdot 30$
1:2	$2 \cdot 0$	$0 \cdot 32$

Table 14. Multipliers for maximum flow velocity

Location	Multiplier
At noses of groynes and guide banks	2·0
At bends	1·5
In straight reaches	1·25

$$F = \frac{U_o}{\sqrt{(gy_o)}} = \frac{4 \times 1\cdot25}{\sqrt{(9\cdot81 \times 3\cdot0)}} = 0\cdot92$$

$$\frac{D_{50}}{y_o} = CF^3 = 0\cdot28 \times 0\cdot92^3 = 0\cdot22$$

$$D_{50} = 3 \times 0\cdot22 = 0\cdot66 \text{ m}$$

Hence stone with a median particle size of 660 mm is required to protect the pier.

The grading of the rip rap should follow a smooth size distribution. Simons and Senturk[12] recommend that the ratio of maximum size to median size D_{50} should be about 2·0 and the ratio between the D_{50} and D_{20} sizes should also be about 2·0 (generally, D_i = size of stone such that $i\%$ of the stones by weight are smaller). The stone should be hard, dense and durable and be able to withstand long exposure to weathering. The thickness of the rip rap should be sufficient to accommodate the largest size of stone.

A filter beneath the rip rap will be required if the underlying material is of such a grading that there is a danger of the fines being washed out through the voids in the rip rap. Filters may be of gravel or of purpose-made plastic cloths. It has been suggested[12] that gravel filters of half the rip rap layer thickness are adequate and that gradings should comply with the following equations.

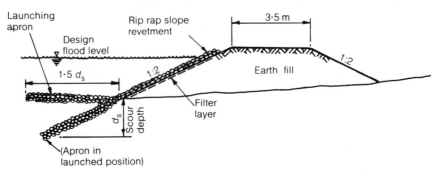

Fig. 14. Typical cross-section through a guide bank with rip rap protection

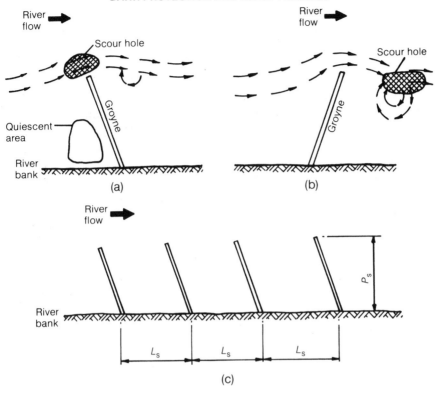

Fig. 15. Groyne layouts: (a) repelling; (b) attracting; (c) typical system for repelling flow

$$\frac{D_{50} \text{ (filter)}}{D_{50} \text{ (base)}} < 40 \qquad\qquad\qquad (43a)$$

$$5 < \frac{D_{15} \text{ (filter)}}{D_{15} \text{ (base)}} < 40 \qquad\qquad\qquad (43b)$$

$$\frac{D_{15} \text{ (filter)}}{D_{85} \text{ (base)}} < 5 \qquad\qquad\qquad (43c)$$

Guide banks and groynes require protection to prevent undermining and collapse of the slope. A common method of protecting the toe of an embankment is to use a launching apron laid horizontally on the river bed adjacent to the toe. As scour undermines the toe, the apron falls and covers the face of the scoured area. Stone sizes for the apron should be the same as for the adjacent slope revetment. Spring[13] recommends a thickness of $1 \cdot 25$ times the largest stone size and a horizontal length such that, in the launched position (assumed to be at a slope of 1:2, reference 7), the apron extends to below the estimated scour depth. A guide bank pro-

59

tected with a typical launching apron is shown in Fig. 14. Alternatively, smaller stones may be used if these are encased in wire or plastic baskets to form a flexible rock mattress.

Groynes

Groynes have a number of functions in river training works but, when used in training work at bridge crossings, they will usually be required either to control the migration of a meander and channel flow through the bridge opening, or to control erosion of the river banks.

Groynes may be concentrated upstream or downstream of the point to be protected either to repel or to attract flow (see Fig. 15(a) and (b)). They are used singly to repel flow and in groups to attract flow. They may also be used in groups to deflect flow, thus protecting a bank, without actually repelling the flow to the opposite bank. The following equation may be used as a guide in spacing groups of deflecting or attracting groynes.[4]

$$L_s < \frac{C\,y^{1\cdot 33}}{2g\,n^2} \tag{44}$$

where L_s = spacing between groynes, m; C = a constant (approximately = $0\cdot 6$); y = mean depth of flow, m; n = Manning's roughness coefficient; g = acceleration due to gravity ($9\cdot 81$ m/s^2).

Other approximate rules for the spacing of groups along a straight river bank may be expressed as

$$L_s = 4\cdot 0P_s \text{ to } 4\cdot 5P_s \tag{45}$$

and

$$L_s = 1\cdot 0B \text{ to } 2\cdot 0B \tag{46}$$

where P_s = length of groynes, m, measured normal to the river bank; B = mean channel width, m.

The spacings given by Equations (45) and (46) may be increased for banks on the inside curve of a bend and decreased on the outside of the curve.

Many factors, other than orientation with respect to the river flow, affect the function of a group of groynes. These include the crest height in relation to bankfull height, whether the heights of all groynes are the same relative to water surface level or whether the heights increase or decrease along the channel, and whether the crests are horizontal or inclined downwards towards the nose of the groyne. These complexities make reliable design difficult without a hydraulic model study, in all but the simplest cases.

When groynes are used to protect a river bank from erosion, they are usually concentrated upstream and their length chosen to achieve the

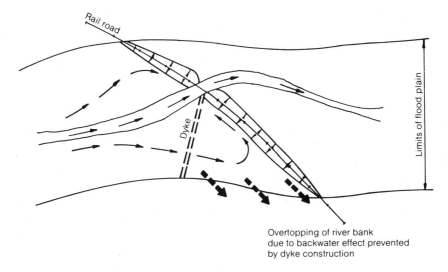

Overtopping of river bank
due to backwater effect prevented
by dyke construction

Fig. 16. Effect of skewed embankment across flood plain

most economic system. Short groynes demand close spacing but the
number may be decreased by increasing their length. The longer the
groyne, however, the deeper and faster will be the flow at the nose and
the more costly the construction. Economic considerations, therefore,
feature strongly in the selection of groyne spacing and length, but
generally groynes for bank protection will not exceed one quarter of the
river width.

When a groyne is required to repel flow to the other bank or when a
series of such groynes is used on alternate sides of the channel to generate
a stable sinuous pattern, the length is typically one third of the channel
width. In the latter case, groynes should be spaced on opposite sides of
the river, at distances apart equal to one half a meander length.

Groynes used to repel flow are of impermeable construction whilst
those used for bank protection may be of permeable or impermeable
construction. Permeable groynes are particularly useful in silt-laden
rivers and quickly encourage sedimentation, so stabilising the bank.
Permeable groynes may comprise a double row of timber piles filled with
cut trees and have the advantage of being cheap. Other types of groyne
construction are steel-piled walls, concrete walls or revetted embankments.

Groynes of embankment construction have side slopes varying from
1:1·25 to 1:3, depending on the construction material, and head slopes
from 1:3 to 1:5. Crest widths will vary from 1 m to 6 m depending on the
scale and method of construction. Crest elevations can vary considerably,
but for groynes designed for crests above the estimated flood level, the
freeboard is usually between 0·5 m and 1 m.

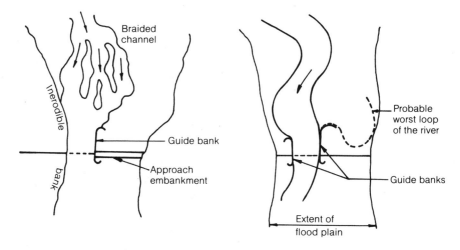

Fig. 17. Use of single and twin guide banks

Dykes

Dykes are embankments designed approximately parallel with the main river channel and have the function of protecting the area behind from flood water. The essential design requirements therefore are that they should be impermeable and high enough to prevent overtopping. If possible they should be located away from the high flow velocity areas, otherwise expensive revetment and groyne works will be required. Typically, dyke side slopes are between 1:2 and 1:5, crest widths are between 2 m and 5 m and crest elevations between 1 m and 2 m above the estimated flood level. Hydraulic model investigations are usually appro- priate in optimising the location of dykes. A case in which a dyke construction is sometimes required is the case of a skewed road or rail crossing over a flood plain. In the example shown in Fig. 16 the dyke construction is required to protect properties and the sections of road or railway on the right bank where flood level is higher than in the bridge waterway by the hydraulic head required to drive the circulating flow.

Guide banks

Guide banks are used to protect the bridge and approaches by guiding and confining the flow through the bridge opening. Two guide banks are generally required when the bridge opening is located in the middle of a wide flood plain. However, in cases where the river meander has been confined by natural control points (i.e. outcrops of inerodible material) on one side of the river, a single guide bank may be sufficient (see Fig. 17).

In the design of guide banks their plan shape, length, cross-section and method of construction must be considered. There is, however, no generalised approach to their design and much of the published information is in the form of general guidance only.

A variety of plan shapes may be selected for the guide banks. For example, they may be straight or curved, parallel or converging, of equal or unequal length, etc. The selection of the most suitable plan shape depends upon the site situation and relies chiefly on past experience. In addition, model studies may be necessary.

The upstream length of the bank should be sufficient to prevent the formation of a meander bend which will endanger the approach embankment, and be sufficient to align the flow parallel to the bridge piers (Fig. 17). The lengths may be assessed by examining the river upstream of the bridge to determine the most acute bend in the meander system and fitting it to the end of the head of the guide bank. The length of the bank can then be chosen so that meander does not endanger the approach embankment.

Neill[10] suggests that in unstable meandering rivers the guide banks should extend upstream from the bridge by three quarters of the bridge waterway width and downstream by one quarter. The bridge waterway width is defined as the clear distance between abutments less than the width of piers projected on to a plane at right angles to the direction of flow. Spring[13] referring to meandering alluvial rivers on the Indian sub-continent, recommends that the upstream bank should be equal to or 10% longer than the bridge waterway width and the downstream bank between one tenth and one fifth of the waterway width. Considerably shorter guide banks are recommended by Andreev[1] (reported by Neill[10]) for flood plain rivers with well defined channels. Andreev's recommendations are based on the ratio of the design discharge to the channel discharge according to Table 15.

The total upstream guide bank length is proportioned between the right and left banks in the ratio of the right and left flood plain discharges. In the case where there is only one guide bank, the total length given is the upstream length of the single bank. The downstream length of the guide banks is made equal to approximately one third of the upstream length.

Some guidance on the design of the heads of guide banks in sand channels may be obtained from references 3 and 13 which indicate radii in the range 150 m – 250 m, with sweeps of between 120° and 145°.

A typical cross-section for a guide bank is shown in Fig. 14. Generally the bank should extend above the estimated flood level, with 0·5 m – 1 m allowance for freeboard. In determining the levels of the top of the guide bank to meet this requirement, the longitudinal variation in the surface water profile should be taken into consideration. The width of the top of the bank should be sufficient to accommodate vehicles. For embankments constructed from earthfill, slope protection will be necessary and

Table 15. Recommendation for guide bank length (after Andreev[1])

Total design discharge*	Total upstream length of guide banks*
Channel portion of the design discharge	Waterway opening
1·0–1·2	0
1·25	0·15
1·5	0·3
1·75	0·45
2·0	0·6
2·5	0·75

*Total design discharge = sum of channel discharge and right and left bank flood plain discharges.
†Total upstream length of guide banks = sum of lengths of right and left upstream guide banks.

an apron will be required to prevent erosion of the toe of the embankment. The design of slope protection and aprons has been discussed above in the section, 'Bank and slope revetment'.

References

1. Andreev, O.V. *Design of bridge crossings*, (in Russian), Ministry of Automobile Transport and Highways.
2. California Division of Highways. *Bank and shore protection in California highway practice*, Dept of Public Works, 1970.
3. Central Board of Irrigation and Power. Manual on river behaviour, control and training. *Publication No. 60*, CBIP, New Delhi, 1971.
4. Delft Hydraulics Laboratory. Improvement of the navigability of the river canal crossing near Wijk bij Duurstede, the Netherlands, morphological aspects. *Report 974–975*, 1973.
5. Gales, R. The principles of river-training for railway bridges, and their application to the case of the Hardinge Bridge over the Lower Ganges at Sara. *J. Instn Civ. Engrs*, 1938, **10**, No. 2, Dec., 136–224.
6. Hydraulics Research Station. *Report on bank protection in rivers and canals*, HRS, Wallingford, July 1980.
7. Inglis, C.C. The behaviour and control of rivers and canals. *Research Publication 13*, Central Waterpower, Irrigation and Navigation Research Station, Poona, 1949.
8. Izbash, S.V. and Khaldre, Kh.Yu. *Hydraulics of river channel closure*, translated from the Revisions by G.L. Cairns, CIRIA, 1970 (originally published in Moscow in 1959).
9. Maynord, S.T. *Practical rip rap design*, US Army Engineers, Waterways Experiment Station, Vicksburg, June 1978.
10. Neill, C.R. *Guide to bridge hydraulics*, Road and Transportation Association of Canada, University of Toronto Press, 1973.
11. Searcy, J.K. Use of rip rap for bank protection. *Hydraulic Engineering Circular No. 11*, Hydraulic Branch, Bridge Division, Office of Engineering and Operations, Bureau of Public Roads, Washington, June 1967.

12. Simons, D.B. and Senturk, F. *Sediment transport technology*, Water Resources Publications, Fort Collins, Colorado, 1977.
13. Spring, F.J.E. River training and control of the guide bank system. Railway Board, Government of India, *Technical Paper No. 153*, 1903.
14. US Army Engineers. Stone stability—velocity vs. stone diameter. *Sheet 712-1*, Civil Works Investigations, Hydraulic Design Criteria, Waterways Experiment Station, Vicksburg, August 1970.
15. US Bureau of Reclamation. Hydraulic design of stilling basins and energy dissipators. *Engineering Monograph No. 25*, Technical Information Branch, Denver, 1958.

Chapter 8

Physical hydraulic models

Introduction

A decision has often to be made on whether or not to use a physical hydraulic model to establish design criteria or to test the effectiveness of a design and possibly improve it. Physical hydraulic models are expensive. They require extensive topographical and hydraulic field surveys, skilled artisans for construction, costly pumps, controls and instruments, and experienced scientific and engineering staff for the design and operation of the model and the interpretation of the results. Physical models are not, therefore, automatically used in the course of designing a crossing over a river.

Model types

Before examining the type of problem for which a model study may be required, it is first necessary to appreciate the types of model which may be constructed. These include: rigid boundary model of the crossing site, river channel, and flood plain with an exaggerated vertical scale; mobile bed model of the crossing site and river channel with some flood plain rigidly moulded—the vertical scale would be exaggerated; flume study of a single bridge pier or two such piers with a mobile bed material using probably a natural scale.

Model application
Rigid boundary model

This would be used to establish backwater effects and current velocities and directions, particularly where the field hydraulic data are limited to values measured at lower discharges. The model would be valuable where the bridge approaches would cause a significant obstruction to flow over the flood plain such that it would be necessary to examine ways of improving the movement of flood water and reducing water levels.

Mobile boundary model

This would be used to establish flow velocities and directions near the proposed piers, at stages above those measured in the field, and the depth of scour as affected by pier shape and orientation. Such a model would be essential if it were necessary to design training works to control the river.

Flume model

This would be used to determine scour depths depending on pier shape and orientation when current directions and velocities are known.

Summary of situations in which a model investigation is advisable

The following are main topics which usually require physical hydraulic models for a satisfactory and reliable solution.

(a) If the Froude number is in excess of about 0.8, a model would predict scour as affected by pier shape and orientation.

(b) Where there are no data on the effect of a particular pier shape on scour or hydrodynamic forces, a model would assist in evaluating the effect and possibly modifying the shape.

(c) Where hydraulic survey data are limited to a narrow range of discharge and water levels, a model would assist in evaluating the effects of extreme flood conditions. Current directions in particular would be studied.

(d) Where current directions are inclined at a large angle to the longitudinal axis of the piers (greater than about $10°$) a model would be desirable.

(e) When road embankments cause a serious obstruction to the movement of flood water across a flood plain or large quantities of water are confined to a narrow waterway, a model would assist in assessing backwater and flood plain flow, and in establishing current directions and scour depths.

(f) A model would assist in predicting the water level where upstream conditions are particularly sensitive to backwater or where upstream channel and flood plain geometry is complex.

(g) A model would assist in developing an economic and effective solution, where a river training scheme may be necessary to control channel movement and to stabilise the current directions near bridge piers.

Chapter 9

Influence of hydraulic factors on the design of bridges over rivers

Introduction

The process for arriving at a final design for a bridge crossing over a river is a complex one in which structural, geotechnical and hydraulic factors are adjusted iteratively to achieve a bridge configuration which is satisfactory functionally, economically and aesthetically. The steps in the process which involve iterative adjustment of the hydraulic factors are illustrated typically in the flow diagram in Fig. 18 and are further discussed below.

Hydraulic factors in a typical bridge design procedure
Step 1

The site reconnaissance and the review and analysis of available river data will enable a selection to be made of possible bridge locations which are compatible with the proposed route of the road or railway (see Chapter 2 for details).

Step 2

At each of the possible bridge locations the hydrographic and hydraulic surveys will be carried out (see Chapter 3 for details).

Step 3

From the available data the following parameters will be assessed

(a) design flood flow
(b) maximum flood level   (see Chapter 4 for details)
(c) navigational constraints on bridge height and pier locations
(d) D_{50}, the median size of bed material (sand bed); D_{90}, the size of material such that 90% of the stones by number are smaller (gravel bed); tractive stress (cohesive bed)
(e) approach flow velocity and direction

(*f*) flood plain width

(*g*) river meander characteristics.

Where it is necessary to make an appraisal of the consequences and cost of the design discharge being exceeded, measured against the additional capital cost of a bridge designed for a flood of a longer return period, the design procedure may be repeated from this step for flood discharges of various return periods.

Step 4 (flood plain crossing only)

The following will be determined within this step of the design process.

Waterway width

For bridge crossings over flood plains, the option to confine the river width should be considered. In the context of this book, a confined river is one which, at the design discharge, flows at a width equal to, or less than, the regime width as calculated from equations presented in Chapter 1. An unconfined river has substantial flood plain flow at the design discharge.

In rivers with meandering channels it is usually cheaper to confine the waterway opening and make the crossing in a combination of embankment and bridge construction than to bridge the full width of the flood plain. A cost comparison quoted in reference 2 and reproduced in part in Table 16, shows that a significant cost saving has been gained in some Indian river crossings by introducing guide banks to confine the flow. A trial waterway opening may be obtained for sand and gravel bed channels by adopting the channel regime widths as calculated from Equations (4) and (6) respectively and from the corresponding figures in Chapter 1. For cohesive bed channels, a trial opening may be obtained by first substituting the maximum measured channel depth at the crossing location into Equation (10) to obtain the discharge per unit width, and then dividing the design flow by the discharge per unit width. The total bridge span may be obtained from the waterway width by making allowance for the obstruction to the flow of the piers and the skew of the bridge to the principal direction of flow. An intuitive allowance for obstruction to the flow by the piers can be made at this point which will be refined at a later step in the design procedure. Allowance for skew will be made if the waterway opening is measured normal to the principal direction of flow.

The effect of decreasing the waterway opening will be to increase the depth and velocity of flow and to make the backwater effect more severe. The spanned length will be correspondingly shorter but the foundations may need to be deeper and must be capable of resisting larger hydrodynamic forces, and the rip rap protection of the guide banks will need to be stronger. Also, depending on the backwater effect, dyke or storage

HYDRAULIC FACTORS IN BRIDGE DESIGN

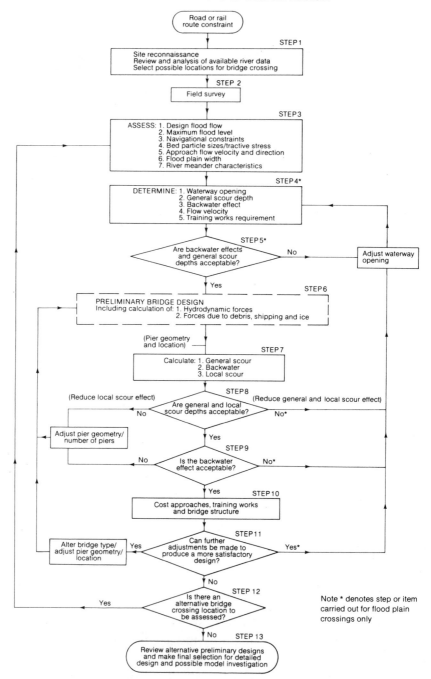

Fig. 18. Flow diagram illustrating hydraulic factors in a typical procedure for design of bridges over rivers

pond construction to prevent overtopping of the river banks upstream may become necessary. It is therefore evident that the economies achieved by decreasing the waterway opening and shortening the spanned length may be offset by increased costs for the foundation and training works, and possibly by increased damage due to raising of flood levels.

General scour depth

The average depth of general scour in a confined waterway may be calculated from Equations (5), (7) or (10) according to whether the channel bed is of sand or of gravel, or of a cohesive material. The maximum depth of general scour may then be obtained by factoring the average depth by the multipliers given in Table 2. For an unconfined waterway the dominant discharge or bankfull discharge may be used to determine the general scour depth from Equations (5), (7) and (10) and Table 2. Alternatively, field measurements of the river channel geometry may be used to assess general scour depths.

Backwater

The backwater effect due to a reduced waterway opening may be calculated at this stage and adjusted for the effects of general scour by the method given in reference 1. A more refined calculation, which will use the pier geometry and location obtained from the preliminary bridge design, will be carried out later in Step 9.

Flow velocity

The flow velocity for incised and unconfined rivers will have been assessed from the field measurements described in the previous step. For a confined waterway, the average velocity may be calculated from the design flow, the width of the waterway and the average general scour depth. The maximum channel velocity may be obtained by factoring the average velocity by the multipliers given in Table 14.

Training works

The requirement for training works will depend on the stability of the approach channel, on whether the waterway opening is being confined and on the nature of the river bank material. In situations where groynes and guide banks are necessary, they will invariably require protection in the form of rip rap. The availability of suitable rock is therefore an important factor when considering the cost of training works. In regions where rock is not readily available, crossing locations which require a minimum of training works will have obvious advantages and, in extreme situations, crossings which bridge the full width of the flood plain may become cheaper to construct than those which confine the waterway openings and require guide banks.

Table 16. Cost comparison of bridges over flood plains

Name of river and location of bridge	Width of flood plain, m	Length of bridge over confined waterway, m	Length of guide bank, m			Ratio of cost of bridge spanning flood plain to cost of bridge over confined waterway and associated training works
			Left	Right	Total	
Krishna at Vijayawada	1463	1138	823	610	1432	1·12
Chenab at Shershaka	3658	1114	1097	1220	2316	2·94
Ganga at Garhmuteshwar	1707	712	466	661	1128	1·65

Table 17. Effect of bridges on meandering dynamically stable channels

Structure	Effect	Result	Design requirements
Embankment	Obstruct drainage in flood plain and increase flow intensity through opening	Local scour at piers and abutments	Increase size of pier and abutment and their foundations Apron/mattress to limit depth of scour
		Increase hydrodynamic force on piers	Increase size of pier and foundations
		Increase upstream water level, and magnitude and frequency of floods upstream	Dyke construction or flood storage
		Local bank erosion	Bank protection
	Obstruct migrating meander	Extensive bank erosion downstream	Bank protection River training upstream
		Scour at toe of embankment on upstream side	Toe protection

Element			
Abutment	Obstruct migrating meander and change pattern	Extensive bank erosion downstream	River bank protection downstream / River training upstream
	Deflect flow pattern and increase local flow intensity	Local scour at abutments	Increase abutment depth or apron/mattress to limit depth of scour / Bank protection
	Reduce width of waterway and increase flow intensity through opening	Local bank erosion downstream	Increase depth of abutment and piers or apron/mattress to limit depth of scour
		Increase scour at abutments, piers and in waterway	
		Bank erosion downstream	Bank protection downstream
		Increase upstream water level and magnitude and frequency of floods upstream	Dyke construction or flood storage
Pier	Deflect flow pattern and increase local flow intensity	Local scour at piers	Increase size of pier and foundations or apron/mattress to limit depth of scour
		Increased hydrodynamic forces on piers	Increase size of pier and foundations or apron/mattress to limit depth of scour
	Reduce width of waterway and increase flow intensity through opening	Increase scour at pier, abutment and in waterway	Increase size of pier and foundations or apron/mattress to limit depth of scour
		Increase upstream water level and frequency of floods upstream	Dyke construction or flood storage

Step 5

At this stage the general scour depths and backwater effect may be reviewed. If general scour depths are such that foundation depths for the bridge and training works are too great, or unacceptable impounding of flood water occurs (reference 3), or the river cannot be contained within the existing banks by a reasonable amount of training works, then it will be necessary to adjust the waterway opening and return to Step 4.

Step 6

In this step in the design procedure, the various alternative types of construction for each possible crossing location will be considered. Their effect on the river regime will be considered and the consequential design requirements, as illustrated in Table 17, will be assessed. Table 17 has been prepared for crossings over meandering dynamically stable channels, but may also be used as a guide in design of crossings over straight and braided river channels. Construction types which are unsuitable for the prevailing conditions will be eliminated, and those which are suitable will be developed to a stage where their cost may be evaluated for comparison purposes.

Many of the factors which will be taken into consideration in the design of a bridge crossing over a river will be common to other types of bridge crossing. These will include

(a) structural loading (deadweight, wind, etc.)
(b) ground conditions
(c) economy of construction
(d) the availability of plant, material and skilled labour
(e) the prevailing climate
(f) access to the site
(g) environmental impact
(h) future maintenance
(i) specific requirements of the Client.

Certain factors apply particularly to crossings over rivers, and can affect the bridge configuration. These are discussed below.

Height of bridge

In cases other than that of the submersible bridge, which is specifically designed to be overtopped for a limited number of days during the year, the clearance between the underside of the bridge and the maximum flood level will be dictated either by navigational requirements or, in a river reach where there is no river traffic, by the freeboard necessary to ensure free passage of debris. The freeboard allowance adopted will largely depend on the tree and vegetation growth on the river banks upstream. In the UK a 1 m freeboard may be considered appropriate, but in tropical rain forest regions a larger freeboard would be more appropriate.

The design levels discussed above relate to the design flood which typically may have return periods within the range 1 in 30 years to 1 in 1000 years. In cases where the freeboard has been kept to a minimum, it may be prudent to check on flood levels for floods with longer return periods. Should the bridge be submerged under these conditions then the effects of uplift and hydrodynamic forces on the bridge deck should be checked.[1]

It should be noted that in some cases the geometric constraints imposed by the bridge approaches will require a minimum bridge level which may be above the minimum level determined from freeboard considerations.

Pier geometry

Pier geometry should be selected after taking due consideration of

(*a*) superstructure loading (deadweight, wind, etc.)
(*b*) wind load
(*c*) type of foundation
(*d*) hydrodynamic forces
(*e*) impact forces (debris, ship, ice)
(*f*) direction of river flow to pier alignment
(*g*) local scour
(*h*) backwater effect
(*i*) aesthetics.

The geometry should be such as to minimise backwater effects and scour. Piers should therefore be aligned with the principal direction of flow and present as small a projected area to the flow as structural and aesthetic considerations allow.

Pier location

Pier location will be dependent on

(*a*) the requirement for safe navigation and the degree of protection required against ship impact
(*b*) the economic span length for the type of bridge construction under consideration
(*c*) ground conditions
(*d*) method of foundation construction
(*e*) channel geometry
(*f*) backwater effect
(*g*) aesthetics.

Under certain circumstances the channel geometry can have a significant influence on the type of bridge construction considered and therefore on the pier locations. Where, for example, a deep, stable flow channel exists over part of the river cross-section a type of bridge construction may be selected which spans the deep channel completely, so avoiding costly and difficult construction within the channel and possible problems due to the effects of local scour.

Step 7

The proposed bridge configuration will be used in this step in the calculation of the general and local scour depths and the backwater effect.

Step 8

The influence of the combined effects of general and local scour in the waterway on the design of the pier foundations will be checked in this step. If a relatively small reduction in scour is required to improve the foundation requirements, then local scour (and in incised river crossings, general scour to a small extent also) may be reduced by adjusting the pier geometry or the number of piers, i.e. returning to Step 6. If a greater reduction in scour is required, then the local and general scour effects will need to be reduced by adjusting the waterway opening, i.e. returning to Step 4.

Step 9

The backwater effect due to obstruction of the flow by the piers will be calculated in this step. For the incised river crossing this will be the first backwater calculation. For the flood plain crossing it will be a refinement on the calculation carried out in Step 4.

If the backwater effect proves excessive, then in the case of the incised river, adjustment to the pier geometry and to the number of piers obstructing the flow will be necessary, i.e. returning to Step 6 and in the case of the flood plain crossing, adjustment to the waterway opening will be necessary, i.e. returning to Step 4.

Step 10

At this stage the design will have been advanced sufficiently for the cost of each of the preliminary bridge designs to be assessed. For confined flood plain crossings the total cost will include the cost of the approach embankments within the flood plain, as well as that of the training works and the bridge structure.

Step 11

The costs of the alternative schemes for each crossing location will be appraised in this step. If the cost of a scheme is outside the budget alloca-

tion, then savings may be possible either by altering the bridge construction by returning to Step 5, or by making adjustments to the waterway
opening by returning to Step 4.

Step 12

If there is an alternative location for the bridge crossing, then the
design process is repeated from Step 3.

Step 13

The alternative bridge designs for each of the alternative bridge crossing
locations will be reviewed and the best scheme selected for detailed
design. Based on the recommendations set out in Chapter 9, a decision
on whether to verify the hydraulic parameters by model investigation will
be made.

References
1. Bradley, J.N. Hydraulics of bridge waterways. *Hydraulic Design Series No. 1*, Bureau of Public Roads, 1970.
2. Central Board of Irrigation and Power. Manual on river behaviour control and training. *Publication No. 60*, CBIP, New Delhi, 1971.
3. George, A.B. Devon floods and the waterways of bridges. *Proc. Instn Civ. Engrs*, Part 2, 1982, 73, Mar., 125–134.

Chapter 10

Case histories

Introduction

The methods discussed in earlier chapters for estimating the hydraulic factors which affect bridge design over rivers do not approach the refinement practised, for example, in structural design, mainly due to the complexities of river interaction with bridge structures. However, the significance of hydraulic factors in the design of bridges over rivers, and their importance in ensuring the safety of such bridges, cannot be underestimated. In a review of bridge failures carried out by Smith,[20] the largest single cause of failure was flood. Of the 143 bridge failures studied, 70 were caused by flood water either undermining foundations or washing away bridge decking. Further examples are illustrated by Neill[14] and others continue to be reported in the literature.[15-17]

The purpose of this chapter is to describe case histories of bridge crossings over rivers which illustrate how hydraulic factors influence bridge design. The case history of the crossing of the Kaduna River, Nigeria, is dealt with in some detail, since many of the hydraulic factors described in earlier chapters were considered in the design. The section describing a crossing of the River Euphrates, Iraq, shows that confining the waterway and reducing the length of the bridge does not always result in the most economical and practical solution. The section subsequent to that describes three situations which illustrate the importance of taking adequate account of the effect of scour when designing temporary river works. These situations also show that in many cases temporary works can be subjected to more severe conditions than the permanent structure.

Kaduna River crossing, Wuya, Nigeria[4-8]

The Kaduna River crossing at Wuya, Nigeria, was designed by Consulting Engineers, Scott, Wilson, Kirkpatrick and Partners. The hydraulic analysis was carried out on their behalf by the Hydraulics Research Station.[5-8]

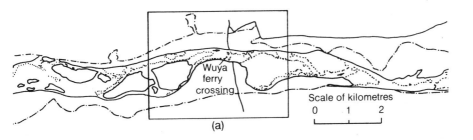

(a)

Scale of kilometres
0   1   2

────── New roads
────── Existing roads
- - - - - Edge of channel at low flow
────── Banks of main river channel
—·—·—·— Approximate extent of mean annual flood
──➤ Direction of flow

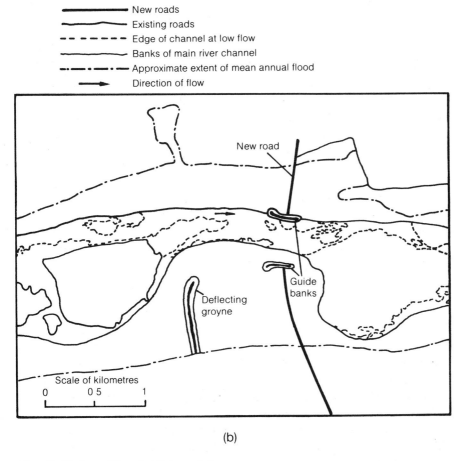

(b)

Fig. 19. Kaduna River bridge crossing

Table 18. Flood analysis results, Wuya

Return period, years	Annual maxima, m^3/s
50	6240
100	6524
200	6888
500	7280
500 (with 20% addition to cover random errors in analysis)	8736

Description of the site

The Kaduna River is located in the southern part of Northern Nigeria. It is a tributary of the Niger with a catchment area of approximately 64 000 km². The bridge is located at Wuya, at the site of an old ferry crossing. The dry season channel is about 200 m wide and meanders between sand banks within a flood plain some 3000 m wide (see Fig. 19).

Estimates of flood discharge

Three methods were used to produce independent estimates of the return periods of floods with a particular discharge at the bridge site. The results obtained are given in Table 18. The design discharge actually adopted by the Consultants was 9900 m^3/s, which has a return period of a little over 500 years. Appoximately, therefore, there is a 1 in 5 chance of the design discharge being exceeded within a 100-year period.

Field measurements and analysis

Field measurements were primarily carried out to gain sufficient data for a hydraulic model investigation. Aerial photographs were used to produce a topographic map of the flood plain over an area 19 km long by 6 km wide, contoured at 1·5 m intervals. Historical sets of aerial photographs were used to examine the meander movement of the river. The mean meander length was determined as 2670 m, the meander belt width as 690 m and the meander rate of migration downstream as 54 m/year.

An existing level gauge at Wuya was supplemented by four other gauges located 3·2 km and 6·4 km upstream and downstream of Wuya. Levels recorded by the gauges were used to estimate the mean water surface gradient as 1 in 4680. Velocity and water level readings were taken in the river channel to supplement information already available and a stage discharge relationship obtained.

The mean water surface gradient, topographic and channel survey data and the stage discharge relationship were used to obtain discharge areas and surface widths at 1·6 km intervals upstream and downstream at Wuya. The information was later used to check the performance of the model.

Measurements of sediment bed load and suspension load were made. It was calculated that 97% of the total sediment load was carried in suspension. Size analysis of samples yielded a D_{50} size for the bed load of 0·569 mm and for the suspended load of 0·014 mm.

Hydraulic river model study

The objectives of the study were to

(a) check the adequacy of the proposed waterway opening
(b) to determine the most economical layout of training works
(c) to determine the effect of the bridge and approach embankments on river levels
(d) to investigate scour at the bridge
(e) to study the requirements for stone protection for training works.

A preliminary model was constructed to a scale of 1:300 horizontal and 1:45 vertical. Adjustments to the model were made until it exhibited a stage discharge relationship, channel depths and widths, meander length, meander belt width and sediment transport rates which compared favourably with those measured in the prototype. The training works proposals were then tested in the model.

The initial trial waterway opening was taken as 448 m which approximates to the regime channel width for the design discharge, as determined from Equation (4). Guide banks were provided on each side of the bridge waterway and a groyne positioned on the right bank, upstream of the bridge crossing, to maintain the river channel on its existing course. The lengths and orientation of the groyne and guide banks were adjusted to achieve optimum flow conditions. The final configuration is shown in Fig. 19. The guide banks were 225 m long, of which 150 m were constructed upstream and 75 m downstream of the bridge. In terms of the waterway opening, the upstream guide banks are approximately one third of the waterway opening and the downstream guide banks approximately one sixth of the waterway opening. The optimum length of the deflecting groyne was found to be 640 m.

Water levels in the model at the bridge waterway, when compared with the stage discharge relationship for the river without the bridge structure, indicated a backwater effect due to the restriction of the bridge and training works of approximately 0·45 m. This relatively large backwater effect had no apparent adverse effect upstream.

At the point in the bridge waterway where the model was subjected to the greatest scour, the depth of flow was measured to be 13·5 m. Some doubt existed at the time over the accuracy of the distribution of general scour in a vertically exaggerated model, so a tolerance of 3 m on model prediction was allowed. The maximum design depth of flow at design discharge was therefore taken as $16 \cdot 5$ m. This compares with a calculated regime depth of $13 \cdot 5$ m ($10 \cdot 8$ m flow depth from Equation (5) factored by $1 \cdot 25$, Table 2).

Velocities measured in the model varied up to a maximum of 3 m/s and directions of flow varied up to a maximum of 10° with the longitudinal axis of the bridge piers.

The optimum size of rip rap for guide banks and groyne protection was determined from a 1:45 natural-scale model specifically designed for the purpose. The model predicted that $275 - 350$ mm equivalent diameter stones would adequately protect the training works, and that launching aprons of the same size stone would launch satisfactorily.

The final conclusion of the river model study was that the waterway opening and training works arrangement would function satisfactorily up to the design discharge. It was considered that no economic or practical advantage would be gained from reducing the waterway any further, and the model results, as described, were used in the final designs. The actual cost of constructing the training works was approximately one half the combined cost of the bridge and the approach embankments within the flood plain.

Assessment of hydrodynamic forces on piers

The assessment of hydrodynamic forces on the bridge piers was made by model experiment. The geometric scale of the model was 1:80, the velocity scale $1:8 \cdot 94$ and the force scale 1:512 000 (i.e. 1 g in the model is equivalent to $0 \cdot 512$ t in the prototype). The pier (Fig. 20) was tested at various angles to the flow of up to 14°, although the maximum angle of skew measured in the model was 10°. At 14° skew, the horizontal force acting along the longitudinal axis of the pier was measured to be 62 t, acting at a height of $0 \cdot 36y$ measured above the bed, and the horizontal force acting transversely to the longitudinal axis of the pier was measured to be 99 t, acting at a height of $0 \cdot 63y$ above the bed (y = depth of flow).

It is interesting to compare the measured forces with those predicted by application of the charts of Apelt and Isaacs, although strictly the pier does not conform with any of the pier shapes on which the charts were based. Assuming the pier to behave as a plate-type pier (Type 4) the charts give a force of 16 t along the longitudinal pier axis and 171 t transverse to it. The assumed shape ignores the pier width, but this is not likely to be significant, in view of the angle of skew. The large difference between model forces and those predicted from the charts can probably be attributed to the assumption that the pile group behaves as a solid body. In computing the moments due the forces, further differences arise because

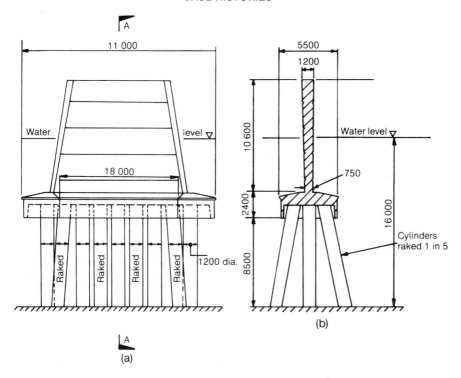

Fig. 20. Kaduna River bridge pier, dimensions in mm: (a) side elevation; (b) section A – A

the points of action of the forces in the model are some distance from the mid-depth point which is the point of action assumed for the chart forces. It may be reasonably concluded from this comparison that such assumptions are likely to lead to poor predictions by the charts.

Local scour at piers

A detailed study of local scour at the bridge piers was not carried out because the piles were founded within a scour-resistant stratum some 5 m below the existing bed levels.

The Ahmad Shah Bridge, Temerloh, Malaysia[11]

The Ahmad Shah Bridge over the River Pahang at Temerloh, Peninsular Malaysia was designed by Consulting Engineers, G. Maunsell and Partners. It is located at the end of a meander in the river where the main channel width is approximately 240 m. Erosion by the river on the outside of the bend is resisted by rock which outcrops a short distance upstream of the site.

Table 19. Flood analysis results, Temerloh

Return period, years	Estimated flood discharge, m³/s
2·5	2830
5	3770
50	5660
500	8490

The catchment area for the River Pahang is about $18\,500\,km^2$ and approximates in shape to an equilateral triangle, with Temerloh about one third the way along its base.

Estimating flood discharge
Rainfall records covering a total of 25 years for four gauging stations within the catchment area were analysed and the Richards formula[18] applied to produce estimates of flood return periods and discharges at Temerloh. The results obtained are given in Table 19.

Bridge configuration
Minimum span requirement
The original bridge at Temerloh had been designed in 17 12 m long spans, as a submersible bridge which would be out of service for only limited periods during the monsoon. In 1961, shortly after the bridge was completed, a major debris jam against the piers and deck occurred, causing the loss of four spans. Some ten years later, a further four spans were lost in similar circumstances. In view of this background, the Client's brief for the new bridge called for a minimum span over the main channel of 150 m to minimise the risk of damage by debris.

Freeboard allowance
The dangers and disadvantages of an unduly low soffit level had unfortunately been demonstrated only too clearly in the case of the original bridge. The soffit level chosen for the new bridge corresponds to the level estimated for a flood with a return period of 500 years. For a flood with a return period of 50 years, the estimated freeboard is 4 m.

Waterway width
The waterway width was calculated from the Lacey formula[10] for a discharge corresponding to the 1 in 500-year flood. A channel width of 230 m was obtained and to this was added an allowance for the obstruction due to the river pier and the effect of the river bend, to give a distance between abutments of 272 m.

Pier locations

The total span requirement of 272 m is achieved in two main spans, 150 m and 122 m long, the larger of which spans the main flow channel on the outside of the bend. The river pier is founded on 1 m dia. cylinders and is located outside the main flow channel in relatively shallow water. The cylinder bases are founded into a rock stratum and the pier designed to be independent of any support from the alluvial deposits and therefore of scour effects.

The Jhelum Bridge, Pakistan[1-3]

The Jhelum River flows within the alluvial plain of the Indus Basin. At the bridge location, alluvial silt overlies layers of kankar, a type of limestone, which in turn overlie beds of gravel. The flood plain is approximately 2440 m wide.

The waterway opening, guide bank lengths and general and local scour levels were determined from a hydraulic model investigation.[2] Modelling was complicated by geological stratification at the bridge site, and by the construction of a new dam located a short distance upstream of the bridge. This dam would intercept river sediment and alter the existing regime conditions.

The bed of the model was constructed in layers of sand, and sand mixed with shingle, to simulate the geological conditions and was positioned below existing levels to take account of the degradation expected following completion of the dam.

The design discharge adopted for the model investigation was 25 000 m³/s, which was the maximum flood recorded at the bridge site. The bridge waterway opening was adjusted in the model to minimise backwater and scour effects. The waterway opening finally selected was 984 m, which is in fact wider than the regime width corresponding to the design discharge. The model showed that the backwater effect for this waterway opening was insignificant.

The guide bank length determined by the model was 822 m which is five sixths of the waterway opening. The guide banks are constructed of earth fill and protected by a stone rip rap layer 0·9 m thick. The rip rap layer acts as an inverted filter and comprises a 150 m layer of 38 mm down crushed stone, a 150 mm layer of quarry spalls, a 225 mm thick layer of nominal sized stone and a top layer 375 mm thick of tightly hand-packed stones, each not less than 36 kg in weight. A launching apron 1·5 m thick and 12 m wide was provided at the toe of each guide bank.

The bridge was designed as a multi-span bridge comprising 22 spans each 45 m long. The piers are founded on 7·6 m dia. brick wells sunk to the founding level. The general scour level (including the effects of degradation) was estimated to be 6·9 m below the existing bed level and the local scour level was estimated to be a further 9·6 m below this. The founding level for the wells was finally taken to 6·4 m below the estimated total scoured depth, i.e. 22·9 m below the existing bed level.

The Fallujah Bridge, Iraq[12]

The bridge crosses the River Euphrates near Fallujah at a location which was chosen to minimise approach roadworks and land expropriation. At the bridge location the river is approximately 450 m wide. The maximum river flow is 3000 m³/s, which is contained between flood banks on either side.

As the river is wider than the regime width for the design discharge of 3000 m³/s (application of the Lacey regime width equation for example[10] gives a regime width of 260 m), consideration was given to confining the waterway opening. A 1:200 horizontal scale and 1:34 vertical scale model was constructed and a feasible arrangement of guide banks was determined which would confine the waterway at the bridge. A 1:45 scale flume study was also carried out to investigate local scour effects at the bridge piers. The model indicated that scour could be expected to a depth of 10 m.

A comparative cost study of the bridge over the unconfined waterway and the bridge over the confined waterway with training works proved to be marginal, and the decision was taken to span the entire waterway between flood banks.

Case histories to illustrate the importance of temporary river works design
Humber Bridge, UK[19,21]

The Humber Bridge is a suspension bridge with two towers and a main span of 1410 m. The tower on one side of the river is founded on a clay layer through soft alluvium, boulder clay and gravel layers some 30 m thick. The construction method adopted was to sink caissons from above maximum water level within a 'figure of eight' sand island enclosed by sheet piles. The island, which was orientated with its longitudinal axis roughly parallel to the river axis, presented a semicircular nose, approximately 22 m in diameter to the main direction of flow. When most of the cofferdam had been driven, a severe storm caused higher river discharges and velocities than expected, and scour of up to 5·5 m at the nose of the cofferdam caused disturbance of the sheet piling. The position was stabilised by tipping 12 000 t of block chalk and sandbags around the base of the piles.

17th July Bridge at Northgate, Baghdad, Iraq[13]

The 17th July Bridge crosses the River Tigris within Baghdad. It is a multi-span bridge with four piers located within the river. During the construction of the bridge a causeway was constructed from the right bank to pier 1 and access jetties were constructed from the causeway and from the left bank to access piers 2 and 4 respectively. The effect of the causeway and jetties was to restrict the river flow and to change the angle of flow to the axis of the piers from one approximately aligned with the flow, to a skew of 20°. An unexpected but relatively modest rise in water levels resulted in the loss of the cofferdam to pier 3.

Crossing of the River Teifi at Cardigan, UK[9]

A study was carried out by the Hydraulics Research Station on behalf of the Transport and Highway Group, Welsh Office, to examine the hydraulic aspects of a proposed crossing of the River Teifi at Cardigan. The section of the report concerned with local scour, predicted scour depths at the piers (2 No. 1 m by 1·75 m columns) to be of the order of 3 m, provided that the pile cap on which the columns are to be founded, is located beneath this scoured depth. The cofferdam required for construction, however, would need to be of the size of the pile cap (approximately 4 m × 16 m) and scour depths in the range 11−17 m were predicted.

References

1. Ahmad, M. Final report on the model of new road bridge on River Jhelum near Jhelum Town. *Tech. Report No. 407/NYD/1963*, Irrigation Research Institution, Lahore, 1963.
2. Fishwick, A.L. Construction of road bridges over the Jhelum and Sutlej Rivers, Pakistan. *J. Instn Highway Engrs*, 1975, Jan.,
3. Fletcher, M. Sir William Halcrow and Partners, private communication, January 1982.
4. Halls, P.N. Scott, Wilson, Kirkpatrick and Partners, private communication, January 1982.
5. Hydraulics Research Station. Kaduna River Crossing—report on field measurements at Wuya. *Report No. Ex 174*, HRS, Wallingford, March 1962.
6. Hydraulics Research Station. Kaduna River Crossing—report on investigation of the relationship of flood frequency and discharge. *Report No. Ex 161*, HRS, Wallingford, October 1961.
7. Hydraulics Research Station. Kaduna River Crossing—report on model investigation of training works. *Report No. Ex 228*, HRS, Wallingford, January 1964.
8. Hydraulics Research Station. Kaduna River Crossing—report on model investigation of hydrodynamic forces. *Report No. Ex 211*, HRS, Wallingford, June 1963.

9. Hydraulics Research Station. *Cardigan By-Pass, bridge over the River Teifi*, Draft report submitted to G. Maunsell and Partners, Consulting Engineers for the Welsh Office, November 1979.
10. Lacey, G. Flow in alluvial channels with sandy mobile beds. *Proc. Instn Civ. Engrs*, 1958, **9**, Feb., 145–164; 1958, **11**, Oct., 219–251.
11. Lee, D.J. and Wallace, A. Ahmad Shah Bridge, Malaysia. *Proc. Instn Civ. Engrs*, Part 1, 1977, **62**, Feb., 89–118.
12. Miller Richards, G. and Pilditch, P. Problems of the design and construction of Fallujah Bridge, Iraq. *Proc. Instn Civ. Engrs*, 1972, **52**, May, 39–56.
13. Morris, M.E. and Hannant, R.B. Some aspects of the design and construction of the 17th July Bridge at Northgate, Baghdad. *Proc. Instn Civ. Engrs*, Part 1, 1979, **66**, Aug., 437–456.
14. Neill, C.R. Guide to bridge hydraulics. Road and Transportation Association of Canada, University of Toronto Press, 1973.
15. *New Civil Engineer*, 20 September 1979.
16. *New Civil Engineer*, 22 October 1981, 4.
17. *New Civil Engineer*, 14 January 1982.
18. Richards, B.D. *Flood estimation and control*, Chapman and Hall, London, 1955.
19. Simm, K.F. Freeman, Fox and Partners, private communication, February 1982.
20. Smith, D.W. Bridge failures. *Proc. Instn Civ. Engrs*, Part 1, 1976, **60**, Aug., 367–382.
21. Wilkinson, G. *Bridging the Humber*, Cerialis Press, 1981.

Chapter 11

Further research

Wherever possible, design guidelines have been given in the preceding chapters which will be of value to the practising engineer. However, in some instances, due to lack of suitable information, conservative approximations have been made in formulating the guidelines. Further research is necessary if greater consistency and economy of bridge design is to be achieved, and topics for this are set out below.

(a) field and experimental studies to determine local scour at abutments and along guide banks
(b) field, experimental and analytical studies to determine local scour effects in cohesive materials
(c) experimental and analytical studies to determine the rate of local and general scour in cohesive, cohesionless and layered materials
(d) experimental studies to determine local scour around pile groups and on pier, pile cap and pile group combinations
(e) experimental studies to determine hydrodynamic forces on pile groups and on pier, pile cap and pile group combinations
(f) experimental studies to determine the extent of rip rap apron required to protect adequately piers and their foundations from local scour
(g) experimental studies to determine guide bank length relationships for different waterway widths, flows and alignments.

Appendix A

Coefficients for the assessment of hydrodynamic forces on bridge piers

Table 20. Designations and proportions of pier cross-sections tested by Apelt and Isaacs (reference 1, Chapter 6)

Cross-section shape	Centre to centre spacing of cylinders / cylinder diameter	Type number*
Twin cylinder	$1 \cdot 625$	2a
Twin cylinder	2	2b
Twin cylinder	3	2c
Twin cylinder	4	2d
Dumb-bell	2	3a
Dumb-bell	3	3b
Dumb-bell	4	3c
Plate pier	$\dfrac{\text{length}}{\text{width}} = 6 \cdot 52$	4

*See Fig. 10.

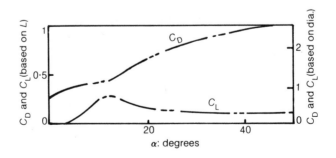

(a) Pier type 2a

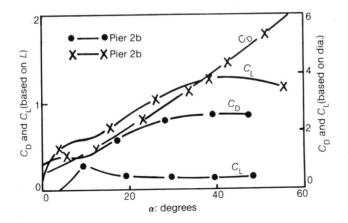

(b) Pier types 2b and 3b

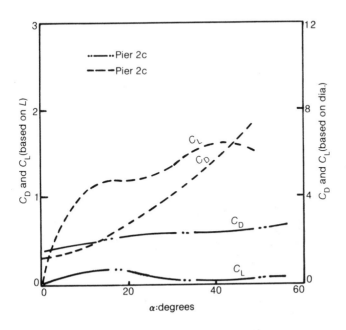

(c) Pier types 2c and 3c

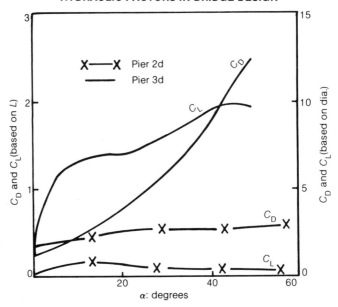

(d) Pier types 2d and 3d

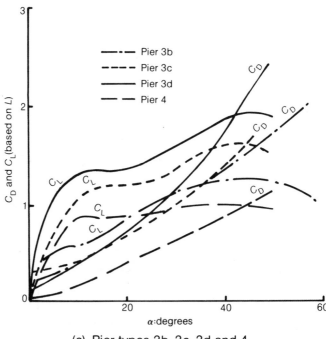

(e) Pier types 3b, 3c, 3d and 4

Charts of C_D and C_L against α for various pier shapes (after Apelt and Isaacs, reference 1 of Chapter 6)

Appendix B

Parameter values used in assessing ice forces (extracted from CAN 3−56−M78, Canadian Standards Association, 1978)

Values for C_n

The Code allows scope for recalculating C_n for angles of inclination greater than 30° based on the bending strength of ice, but does not suggest a method of calculation. This point is further discussed in reference 12 of Chapter 6, see Table 21.

Effective strength p

The effective ice strength is normally taken in the range 700−2800 kPa according to the following guide.

(a) In the order of 700 kPa where break-up occurs at melting temperatures and where the ice runs as small 'cakes' and is substantially disintegrated in its structure.

(b) In the order of 1400 kPa where break-up occurs at melting temperatures, but the ice moves in large pieces and is internally sound.

(c) In the order of 2100 kPa where at break-up there is an initial movement of the ice sheet as a whole or where large sheets of sound ice may strike the piers.

(d) In the order of 2800 kPa where break-up or major ice movement may occur with ice temperature significantly below the melting point.

Table 21. Inclination coefficients

Inclination inwards towards top of pier nose to vertical, degrees	Coefficient, C_n
0−15	1·0
15−30	0·75
30−45	0·5

Table 22. Pier coefficients; b = pier width or pile diameter, t_i = design ice thickness

b/t_i	Coefficient
0·5	1·8
1·0	1·3
1·5	1·1
2·0	1·0
3·0	0·9
4·0 or greater	0·8

The preceding values for effective ice strength are to be used with piers of substantial mass and dimensions. The values are to be modified as necessary for variations in pier width, pile diameter, and design ice thickness by multiplying by the appropriate coefficient obtained from Table 22. For further details the reader is referred to the Code.

Appendix C

Conversion of the volume of deformed steel at the collision point, R_s, into a depth of damage penetration, P_i (after Minorsky, reference 9 of Chapter 6)

In calculating the volume of deformed steel of the vessel, R_s (also called the resistance factor), during a head-on collision with a pier/fender, the deformation of the following structural members of the vessel is considered

(a) deck, flats and double bottom
(b) longitudinal bulkheads
(c) hull, this volume is factored by $0 \cdot 7$ to account for the curvature of the bow.

Transverse bulkheads are neglected since their resistance to deformation is low in the head-on collision. R_s is defined as

$$R_s = (M_n L_n t_n)_{\text{decks}} + (M_n H_n t_n)_{\text{bulkheads and hull}} \tag{47}$$

where M_n is the depth of damage in the nth member of the colliding vessel, m; L_n is the length of damage in the nth member of vessel, m; t_n is the thickness of nth member of vessel, m; H_n is the height of damage in the nth member of vessel, m.

In assessing the penetration depth, the details of the structure of the 'design' vessel for the impact study are required. An initial estimate is made of the overall depth of penetration of the pier/fender into the vessel P_i, and the volume of deformed steel R_s, calculated for this penetration using Equation (47). The width of the damage may be assumed to be equal to the width of the pier/fender. For fender collision the height of the damage may be assumed to be the height of the fender, and for pier collision it may be assumed to be the depth of vessel from uppermost continuous deck. If this value of R_s is approximately equal to the R_s derived from Equations (38), (39) and (40) or (41) (Chapter 6), then the penetration selected is used to calculate the average impact force. If not, the initial estimate of P_i must be modified and R_s recalculated until it matches the value of R_s from the above equations.

In cases where the width of pier is greater than the ship's beam and the entire bow can be assumed to be crushed on impact, then the following approximation may be used to determine the depth of damage penetration.

$$R_s = P_i S_v \qquad (48)$$

where S_v = volume of steel per metre length of vessel, m².

Appendix D

Notation

a catchment area, km^2

A area of cross-section, m^2

A_c number of collisions per year

b width of pier or diameter of pier, m

B mean channel width, m

B_m meander breadth, m

C coefficient

C_n coefficient of nose inclination

C_D drag coefficient

C_L lift coefficient

d_s depth of scour measured below upstream bed level, m

D characteristic bed particle size, m

D_{15} size of bed material such that 15% of the stones by number are smaller, m

D_{20} size of bed material such that 20% of the stones by number are smaller, m

D_{50} median size of bed material, m

D_{85} size of bed material such that 85% of the stones by number are smaller, m

D_{90} size of bed material such that 90% of the stones by number are smaller, m

e voids ratio of the soil mass

E energy absorbed on ship impact, kNm

f_2 factor to take account of pier shape

f_3 factor to take account of pier skew to direction of flow

$f(a)$ area reduction factor

F Froude number

F_D drag force, N

F_E entrainment function

F_H horizontal ice force, kN

F_L lift force, N

F_s side factor to describe bank toughness

g acceleration due to gravity ($= 9 \cdot 81 \, \text{m/s}^2$)

H rainfall constant, mm

H_n height of damage of nth member of the vessel, m

i average rainfall intensity over a given area, mm/h

I rainfall intensity at a point, mm/h

J ship's beam, m

k hydrodynamic supplementary mass coefficient

K runoff coefficient or constant

L pier length, m

L_c length of catchment, km

L_m meander wave length, m

L_n length of damage in the nth member of the vessel, m

L_s spacing between groynes, m

m order of ranking (in flood reoccurrence relationship)

M_n depth of damage penetration in nth member, m

n Manning's roughness coefficient

N factor based on shape of storm

p effective ice strength, kN/m^2

P wetted perimeter, m

P_i depth of damage penetration, m

P_d pressure, kN/m^2

P_s length of groyne, m

q discharge per unit width, $\text{m}^3/\text{s/m}$

q_o discharge per unit width upstream of pier, $\text{m}^3/\text{s/m}$

Q discharge, m^3/s

Q_D dominant discharge, m^3/s

r number of years of records

R hydraulic radius, m

R_c risk factor

R_s volume of deformed steel, m^3

R_* particle Reynolds number

s specific gravity of soil particles

S hydraulic gradient, or slope of main stream

S_v volume of steel per metre length of ship, m^2

t time of concentration, h

t_i thickness of ice in contact with pier, m

t_n thickness of nth member of vessel, in

T storm duration, h

T_c traffic in ship transits through the bridge each year

T_r return period, years

U average flow velocity, m/s

NOTATION

U_c average critical velocity for initiating sediment motion

U_o approach velocity, m/s

U_* shear velocity, m/s

V ship's velocity, m/s

y mean depth of flow, m

y_o depth upstream of pier or bank, m

α skew angle of pier to direction of flow, degrees

γ specific weight of fluid, N/m^3

ν kinematic viscosity, m^2/s ($= 1 \cdot 14 \times 10^{-6}$ for water at 15°C)

ρ mass density of water, kg/m^3

τ_c critical tractive stress, N/m^2

Γ_o bed shear stress, N/m^2 ($= \gamma RS \approx \gamma yS$ for wide channels)

Δ ship's displacement, t

Index

INDEX